# FOOTPRINTS ON THE MOON

# FOOTPRINTS

By the Writers and Editors of

THE ASSOCIATED PRESS

Manuscript by John Barbour

# ON THE
# MOON

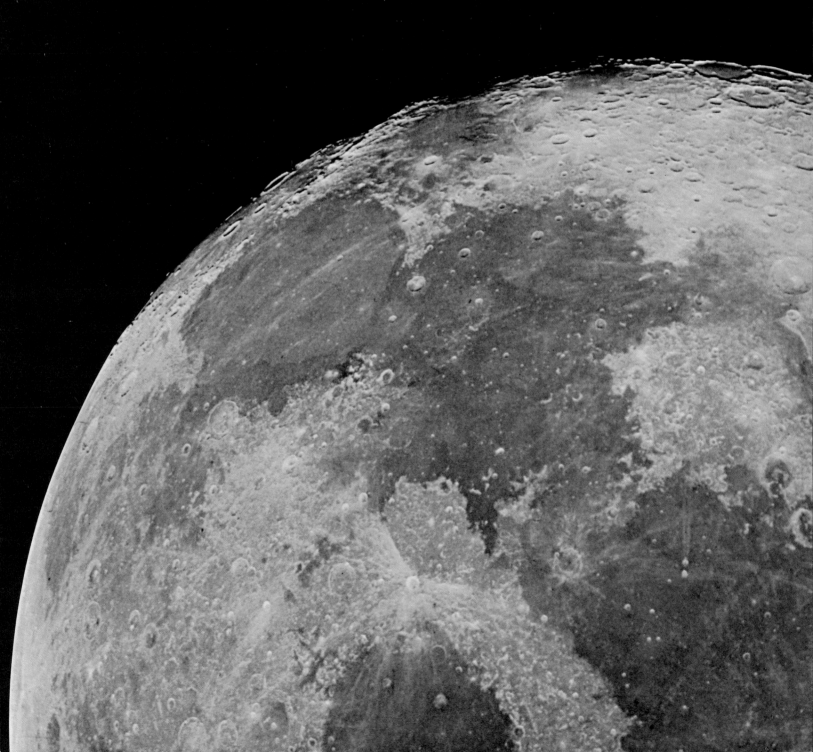

*Project Director:* Keith Fuller

*Editorial Supervisors:* Dan Perkes, Nate Polowetzky, M. J. Wing

*Photo Editor:* Sandy Colton

*Text Editor:* Norman Goldstein

*Technical Assistance:* Howard Benedict, James Strothman,
Alton L. Blakeslee, Paul Recer

*Photographs:* The Associated Press staff, NASA, Tass
and Novosti

*Book Design:* Sidney Feinberg

*Promotion:* Ed Fleming

Manufactured in the United States of America
by American Book–Stratford Press, Inc.

# Contents

# Foreword

"Tranquillity base here. The Eagle has landed."

With these words, three intrepid space explorers made our lives unique in history by taking the first giant step to the stars—a landing on the moon.

In an era marked by wars and human strife, the astronauts gave people of the world a spiritual lift by making the major news event of this century one of man's achievements rather than his failures.

This book, therefore, is dedicated to Astronauts Armstrong, Aldrin and Collins and their myriad technical experts who made the flight possible.

Wes Gallagher
*General Manager*

# FOOTPRINTS ON THE MOON

# 1  The Decision

Eight days after the Soviets propelled the first human being into space, just one day after the Bay of Pigs ended in America's humiliation, the 35th President of the United States wrote this memorandum to the man who would one day be the 36th President of the United States:

MEMORANDUM FOR THE VICE PRESIDENT

In accordance with our conversation I would like for you as Chairman of the Space Council to be in charge of making an over-all survey of where we stand in space.

1. Do we have a chance of beating the Soviets by putting a laboratory in space, or by a trip around the moon, or by a rocket to land on the moon, or by a rocket to go to the moon and back with a man? Is there any other space program which promises dramatic results in which we could win?

2. How much additional would it cost?

3. Are we working 24 hours a day on existing programs? If not, why not? If not, will you make recommendations to me as to how work can be speeded up.

4. In building large boosters, should we put our emphasis on nuclear, chemical or liquid fuel, or a combination of these three?

5. Are we making maximum effort? Are we achieving necessary results?

I have asked Jim Webb, Dr. Wiesner, Secretary McNamara and other responsible officials to cooperate with you fully. I would appreciate a report on this at the earliest possible moment.[1]

JOHN F. KENNEDY

It was dated April 20, 1961.

With that memo, John Kennedy cranked up the ponderous mill of federal decision-making that ultimately would send the United States on its way to the moon, spend more than $25 billion of public money, harness the adventure and test the faith of

1. From the forthcoming book, "We Should Go To The Moon: Project Apollo and National Decision-Making," M.I.T. Press, by John M. Logsdon, assistant professor of politics, Catholic University.

some, arouse the doubt and anger of others. In less than 200 words, he set the wealthiest nation in history toward a goal that poets had dreamt of, that primitives had worshipped.

The moon, strange silver ball in the sky, full of romance and superstition, keeping the same face toward the earth as it circled, as if taking the measure of man. It governed the tides of earth's oceans, measured the fertility cycles of earth's women, gave mankind a magical name for madness. But now it became more; it became the focus of a nation's pride.

And finally, in July of 1969, after eight years of transient triumph and recurrent despair, an American would set foot on the moon, the first human to test its sun-baked, crusty soil. In this lunar desert with its blinding white surface, its stark black shadows, its small gray compromises, he would plant a flag, as is the manner of men to do, and would give the world a thrill to last the ages—man's first step into the starry night of space, to a kingdom he had always relegated to God. Now it was, as well, the realm of man.

Yet so oddly, this all began with hurt national pride, with a sudden fearsome imbalance in earthly power, and with the political pragmatism of one man who realized that the United States could not be second in the eyes of the world, because second was last.

He could not realize at first that the strength of trying would be almost as important as the winning itself. He could not know that the knowledge and the riches would spread through the fabric of American life. He could not see that ultimately there would be the promise of knowing the weather 14 days in advance, the ability to prospect the earth for hidden riches from 100 miles above. No one could know then that man one day would watch from space to see the migration of shrimp, the withering of forest or wheat field, that he would map a nation or a continent in an afternoon, and use his new-found prominence for a hundred and one tasks that the view from the highest hill afforded.

To John Kennedy, the competitor, faced with Communist threats in Southeast Asia, with shameful defeat in Cuba, with frightening immobility and division at home, there was no time to linger with bitterness and self-pity. The moon was a goal, something the eyes could see, something common men could believe in, something Americans could win, and with its winning, find vigor in an exhausting world.

The idea was not the President's. The decision was not made overnight. It was the slow work of a hundred committees and teams, a thousand ambitious minds. But the events of early 1961, with the belabored new administration searching for meaning, put the weight of a nation behind the dreams and plans of others. It was, if anything, overdue.

As a matter of national conscience it had begun nearly three years and four months before John Kennedy took office. It was then that a bewildered but lethargic America watched as its own puny space rockets fizzled on the launch pads while the Soviet Union, supposedly a rural autocracy, seemed to fill the air with satellites.

October 4, 1957. Sputnik. A miracle and a threat all in one. Hear it up there beeping? The whole world could hear it. As one space scientist, a man who would later help guide the way to the moon, put it, "The realization that the Russians weren't just a bunch of Tartars riding around on horseback out on the Siberian Steppes was brought home very vividly." Not just to America, but to the world. On November 3, 1957, the Soviets launched a dog named Laika into space in Sputnik II. James E. Webb, who would one day head the U.S. space agency, remembers being in Oklahoma City then: "I remember the minister the next morning, preaching a sermon in which he said the world will never be the same. There's life up there now."

The Sputniks brought cries of shock from Congress, from Republicans and Democrats alike, shouts for action, for reappraisal, damning the American preoccupation with material things, with the height of a car's tail fins, with the depth of pile on a new broadloom rug. There were calls for sacrifice, for changes in everything from education to the values of life. But in spite of the shouting, the nation moved slowly.

The first two Soviet Sputniks weighed a total of 1,300 pounds. The United States was still trying and failing to launch a 3¼-pound sphere called Vanguard. It wasn't until January of 1958 that a frustrated band of German rocket experts working for the U.S. Army were allowed to do what they had pleaded four years to do—launch a satellite. Even then the U.S. offering to space was pitifully small, less than 31 pounds, although it discovered grand mysteries about the earth.

And so it went. The cost-conscious Eisenhower administration stuck to its position that there was no space race, but the headlines and television bulletins kept reminding the American people there was. Finally, in October of 1958, a year after Sputnik I, the United States created a space agency, the National Aeronautics and Space Administration, underfunded, understaffed, with only an inkling of what space was all about. But it was a start.

Within two years the so-called missile gap and the space gap were prime political issues, and John Kennedy, running for the presidency against Richard Nixon and the

Eisenhower record, played them against each other, bouncing his charges of neglect off the headlines of Soviet success and U.S. failure.

Yet when he took office he was not only naive on space matters, but so were many on his staff. And they were preoccupied with Communist incursions on earth, the near-defeat of a U.S.-backed regime in Laos, the Fidel Castro takeover in Cuba. Besides, the United States by now had a fledgling man-in-space program, Project Mercury, and seven astronauts aching to fly. The U.S. hoped it would place a man in orbit before the end of 1961. That seemed adequate. Anything more seemed too expensive. In his inaugural address, Kennedy sounded a theme he would stick to for the weeks ahead. To the Russians he said, "Let us explore the stars together."

But the Russians were more keenly aware of the race they were winning. True, the United States up to 1961 had launched 33 satellites to only nine for the Soviets. But those nine Soviet satellites outweighed all of the U.S. orbitings by more than 2-to-1. And while the United States had discovered the great belts of radiation in space and discovered the effect of firing nuclear warheads into near space, the Soviets had flown living creatures, dogs, around the earth. There was no question but that they were aiming to do the same with a man.

Dwight D. Eisenhower had cut the last space agency budget in his administrative tenure, had bluntly told the nation it would not support any extended flights beyond the one-seater Mercury spaceships designed to orbit the earth. To the space agency, it was a disappointment. The U.S. designers announced in July, 1960, plans for another project called Apollo, which could send three men into an extended earth orbit, or carry them out on a trip around the moon. The Eisenhower decision meant they could not start work on these more ambitious goals yet. When he came to office, John Kennedy did nothing to change that. He concentrated on problems closer to home.

In fact, most of the early reports by his task forces were highly critical of the space agency, and warned that the nation should stop advertising its upcoming Mercury flights because if a man were lost in space or on the launch pad it would seriously damage U.S. prestige. There were, and there had been, voices in Congress urging suport for the U.S. manned space flight program, but they were lost in the welter of problems besetting the new administration.

Then on April 12, 1961, there was Yuri Alekseyevich Gagarin. The President had been forewarned. Moscow buzzed with rumors as early as April 10 that a Russian had been shot into space. Kennedy knew that the Soviets were testing a new five-ton spaceship, that it had begun in failure, but that its record had improved dramatically. Before he went to bed on the night of April 11, he was told the Soviets would launch a man into space before morning. They did.

Gagarin completed one orbit of the earth in a new Vostok spaceship on April 12, and then re-entered the earth's atmosphere safely, parachuting to earth. The next day Kennedy heard Gagarin issue a boastful challenge, "Now let the other countries try to catch us."

The world marveled at the Russian feat. It was applauded by heads of state and men on the street, by the American President and the American astronauts. A nation used to producing heroes such as Charles Lindbergh for the world had to swallow hard at the earth's newest hero, the first man into space, Soviet citizen Maj. Gagarin.

Three weeks before the Soviet success, President Kennedy had agreed to hear space agency arguments for an additional $300 million for its annual budget. The Budget Bureau would agree to only $50 million. Kennedy upped it to $125 million, but denied funds directly aimed at a moon program, except for the development of bigger rocket boosters.

On the evening of Gagarin's victory, essentially the same cast of characters present at the earlier budget meeting met again in the White House. Kennedy had a late interview with Hugh Sidey of *Life* magazine, and perhaps to show Sidey his concern for the problem, invited him along to hear the discussion. It was something of an embarrassment for James Webb, the new space agency chief. "My recollection is that President Kennedy wanted us to come over there to talk about space, and I was very surprised to find Sidey there," Webb said, "because it didn't seem to me that this was a proper way to talk about important national policy and I wasn't anxious to proceed into a detailed discussion with him there."

On the same day the President had received a new report on Project Mercury which acknowledged that the first flight would be "a high risk undertaking but not higher than we are accustomed to taking in other ventures," risks the Wright Brothers took, that Lindbergh took. But that report apparently did not enter the conversation. Kennedy was looking further ahead.

Sidey's account of the meeting in his 1964 book, *John F. Kennedy, President*, shows the groping of the new President, short on facts and advice, wary of costs and national temper, but facing still another Soviet challenge.

The others stood when the President entered the Cabinet room—Webb; David E. Bell, director of the Bureau of the Budget; Dr. Jerome Wiesner, chief science adviser; Hugh Dryden, deputy administrator of NASA, and Theodore Sorensen, the President's adviser. Kennedy pulled out the black leather chair normally reserved for the Secretary of the Interior near the end of the big mahogany table. He tilted back in the chair and put his rubber-soled shoe on the table's edge for balance. His questions were direct: "What can we do now?"

He frowned as the experts recited the dismal state of the nation's space affairs. "We may never catch up," he said.

Finally he asked, "Is there any place where we can catch them? What can we do? Can we go around the moon before them? Can we put a man on the moon before them?"

Dryden said the one hope was a crash program that might cost $40 billion, and then there would be no guarantee.

"The cost," Kennedy said. "That's what gets me."

Then, Sidey relates, the President turned again to the men around him. He was silent a moment. Then he said, "When we know more, I can decide if it's worth it or not. If somebody can tell me just how to catch up. Let's find somebody—anybody. I don't care if it's the janitor over there, if he knows how."

He paused again, scanning their faces. "There's nothing more important."

It is doubtful if space matters had Kennedy's sole attention on April 12. At a news conference earlier that day he told one questioner that there would be no intervention in Fidel Castro's Cuba by U.S. armed forces "under any condition." But just two days earlier a brigade of U.S.-armed Cuban exiles moved to a Nicaraguan port to board ships for an invasion of their homeland. On April 17, five days after Gagarin's flight, the brigade, sponsored by the U.S. Central Intelligence Agency, hit the beach at the Bay of Pigs. The ensuing disaster lasted only two days, with Castro's forces tearing the ill-equipped exile force to shreds, and leaving the United States and its President in shame, shock and disarray.

The effect reached deep into the Kennedy administration and into the whole cloth of government. But if others could afford the luxury of self-recriminations, Kennedy, after admitting folly, would not allow further brooding. On April 20, the day after the final Bay of Pigs remnants were withdrawn, he met extensively with a number of people including Vice President Lyndon B. Johnson. He concluded the day with his memorandum and the orders to find the answers in space.

The Vice President liked the assignment. He had been close to the space program in the Senate, was a chief author of the Space Act, had sometimes been critical of the slow progress. He stepped in at a time when the space agency was pressing for the first manned test flight of its Mercury spacecraft, sending the first American on a 15-minute ride some 290 miles out into the Atlantic, and a brief visit to the edge of space. The launch date had slipped again and again. Now, if everything went right, it was set for May 2, 1961.

But Johnson's job dealt with the future. He began what Webb recalled was "a constant flux of meetings and talk and discussions and examination and work at night, and more discussion with congressmen and senators . . . I'd say hardly an hour or part of a day went by that there were not many, many different phases of activity going on."

From his telephone, Johnson called in outside people and inside people. What was practical in terms of cost? What would have the support of Congress? What was technically feasible? How would the American people feel about it? The questions went on and on. Johnson was the discussion leader, the consensus-maker, and all of the talents he had developed in the Senate went into the job.

Many of the meetings were held under the aegis of the National Aeronautics and Space Council of which Johnson was chairman. On April 28, the council submitted a tentative report to the President. It said in essence: "The moon is a good target for us."

Dr. Edward Welsh, then executive secretary of the council, listed the reasons:

—It was something nobody had yet done.

—It was something neither the Soviets nor we were able to do at the time.

—It was something we had at least some chance of doing first.

—It was a chance to go someplace—the nearest place we could go out into space—albeit a quarter of a million miles away.

—It would help regain international prestige by doing something first instead of second (and of course this would influence the reaction abroad toward the efficiency and effectiveness of democracy and capitalism as against a centralized dictatorship).

—It would cause us to develop a whole series of capabilities, which, once developed, could be used for a wide variety of jobs in space.

"There was not very much of the idea that it was awfully important to go to the moon for its own sake," Welsh said.

The next day the President called in a group including Welsh to talk in general about the space race. The shadow of the Bay of Pigs still hung over many of Kennedy's advisers, and what it had done to the image of America. No one liked the idea of risking that image further. But the space agency was all but ready for the first Mercury flight, and had announced that the astronaut would be either John H. Glenn Jr., Virgil I. Grissom, or Alan B. Shepard Jr., the names always listed alphabetically. Public interest was running high, and some Americans were already drawing lots as to which astronaut it would be.

More than half a dozen men gathered in the President's office. Someone, Welsh recalled, one of the President's advisers, raised the question of postponing the flight. If

First Men In Space—Yuri Gagarin was first and flew round the earth on the first Soviet try. Alan Shepard (left) paid a 15-minute visit to the fringes of space. The United States had to try harder because it was No. 2.

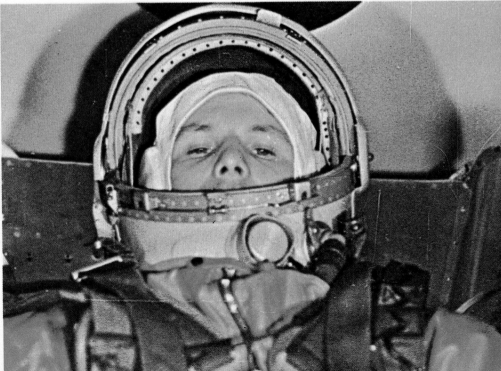

Number One—The Russians had the rocket muscle and used it to launch its Sputniks first, and later, with augmented engines, hurled its Vostok spaceships and their pilots into orbit.

Number Two—The Americans had to settle for brief rides aboard the Redstones, pencil-like military rockets pressed into space service to test the Mercury spacecraft.

it failed, he said, it could hurt U.S. prestige abroad even more. But Welsh was confident. It wouldn't fail, he said, and "why postpone a success?"

"Are you that confident it will be successful?" the President asked.

"I don't think the risks are any greater than flying from here to Los Angeles in bad weather," Welsh replied.

The President made no attempt to endorse the pessimism. The launch date stood.

But pessimism was not restricted to the Kennedy advisers. The surge of public feeling had others worried. On the floor of the Senate on May 1, Republican Sen. John J. Williams of Delaware called for a postponement too, with a secret launch date set in the future: "We are witnessing another tremendous buildup of a project which, if successful, will represent a great step forward in American space exploration, but which, if a failure, will be looked upon as another American fiasco."

The point concerned many. It was a calculated risk. The Soviet shots were conducted in secret. The American shots were to be conducted in view of everyone and anyone from the sandy spit of land jutting into the Atlantic, Cape Canaveral, Fla.

Well before the launch, the American people read and heard all of the specifics of the flight. They learned who the range safety officer was, a red-haired Air Force captain who could cut off the flight with the flick of a switch if it began to go awry. They read about the elaborate escape system with its own rocket that could, technicians hoped, pull the astronaut to safety. They read that another man would watch the rocket climb between two vertical wires to see how far it was straying from normal, an oddly primitive way, it seemed, to chart man's way into space.

They learned that a representative of the Federation Aeronautique Internationale would be at Cape Canaveral to verify the flight for world records. They took some satisfaction when he said that the Soviets had applied for records on the Gagarin flight, but would not have them listed until they provided more details from their secret launch.

They learned that the Redstone rocket which would hurl the astronaut into space was called "Old Reliable" by the experts, that it was 83 feet tall and weighed 33 tons and was loaded with kerosene and oxygen to burn in the oxygen-sparse altitudes it would reach. It was the same rocket that had taken a chimpanzee named Ham on an earlier, similar flight, but had climbed too steeply, and gone too far, and given Ham too rough a ride. Indeed, they learned everything about the flight except the astronaut's name. For some odd reason, perhaps to prevent too close an identification with him should something happen, that was kept a secret.

With the nation standing by the television screens on May 2, the American public got another education in space age erratics—weather and postponement. Heavy clouds moved in over the Cape area and out to sea. Launch officials who wanted a clear view of the rocket all the way up and all the way down decided to wait for a better day. But before they did, the name of the astronaut leaked out, and they confirmed it—Navy Cmdr. Alan Bartlett Shepard Jr., a 37-year-old native of East Derry, N.H.

The public learned all about him. He drove a white sports car with racing tires, was a water ski expert with an I.Q. between 135 and 147. He stood 5-feet-11, weighed a lean 160 pounds. His reading habits included technical manuals and policy journals, "the kind," his wife Louise said, "the admirals and generals say should be read." He was a Naval Academy graduate whose father was a retired Army colonel. He was a Navy test pilot with 3,700 hours in the air. He was the father of two young girls. When asked if he was ready to fly into space, he said, "Yes, the answer is an overwhelming yes—a resounding yes."

Such was the thirst of a nation tired of being No. 2 in space. Such was the hunger for a new hero. Such was the climate of 1961 as John Kennedy measured America's future in space.

On May 4, the skies over Florida cleared dramatically. Shepard and his backup pilot, John Glenn, ate dinner together in the gray-walled dining room of the forward medical area at the launch site. They returned to their quarters in Hangar S and Shepard watched television before retiring at 10:30 p.m. Forty-eight minutes before midnight the ring of giant floodlights around the Redstone rocket turned night into day. Shortly after midnight the final countdown began. Shepard awoke at 1:05 a.m., showered, shaved, dressed in long, lightweight, white underwear, then break-fasted on a seven-ounce filet mignon wrapped in bacon, two poached eggs and orange juice. A Christian Scientist, he did not see the Protestant chaplain assigned to him. After a physical examination his spacesuit was tested for leaks. He arrived at the launch pad at 4:26 a.m. At 5:18 he entered the space capsule above the fuming Red-stone rocket, with dawn brightening the sky over the Atlantic. One minute before 9 a.m., a horn sounded and all personnel were cleared from the launching area, leav-ing Shepard, his spaceship and the loaded rocket standing alone.

In Mercury Control, 15 men sat behind three banks of electronic consoles listening with headsets to the rapid-fire voices checking off the last items, watching the panels and scopes for signs of anything wrong.

A switch was thrown, a button pressed. A panel flashed green.

With a nation waiting, at 34 minutes after 9 on May 5, 1961, the rocket blasted off the pad. Shepard was on his way, the vibration of the rocket blurring his vision. America seemed to be riding with him. In Manhattan, at the Criminal Courts Build-ing, attorneys and policemen clustered around a radio. "Go, go, go," one of them mur-mured. "Atta boy," said someone else. "Pray for him," said a third. Traffic slowed on the Los Angeles freeways, and the car radios seemed to speak with one voice. A Philadelphia judge interrupted a trial to announce Shepard was alive and safe. The Iowa Legislature all but suspended its windup session to listen to the news. In India-napolis, a court hearing a case on the theft of a television set used the set to watch the flight.

In Washington, the President and the National Security Council suspended dis-cussions and watched breathlessly on television, heard the first words from the rising spacecraft that Shepard called Freedom 7. It was the astronaut reading out the cabin

After Dinner With John Glenn—Shepard walked into the final countdown of America's first manned flight. It came more than a month after Gagarin's orbit of the earth, but succeed or fail, it was done in full view of the world.

pressure, the acceleration forces, the temperature, the fuel levels. Meaningless as the technical details were to most of the listeners, everyone hung on every word. Then the rocket burned out and fell away. For nearly five minutes Shepard felt the eerie sense of weightlessness. "What a beautiful sight," he said as he saw the East Coast of the United States strung out behind and below him, the white-edged, green headlands against the turquoise ocean. Then his words became grunts as he endured the braking forces pulling at him, the spacecraft plunging again into the earth's dense blanket of air. He splashed down 302 miles out in the Atlantic after a trip 115 miles high. Shepard crawled out of his bobbing spaceship and was hoisted aboard a Marine helicopter. How was it? "Boy, what a ride!" he told the crew. Aboard the aircraft carrier *USS Lake Champlain* he told doctors, "I don't think there's much you'll have to do to me."

On impulse, President Kennedy placed a radio-telephone call to the ship and began gratefully, "Hello commander . . . I wanted to congratulate you very much . . . We watched you on TV, of course, and we are awfully pleased and proud of what you did." Shepard replied, "Well thank you, sir. As you know by now, everything worked out just about perfectly. And it was a very rewarding experience for me and for the people who made it possible." Kennedy invited Shepard to Washington and said, "The members of the National Security Council are meeting on another matter this morning, and they all want me to give you their congratulations."

A whole nation and half a world gave a collective sigh of relief. The trip cost each man, woman and child in America the grand sum of $2.25. The universal reaction

"Up And Down Alive"— Shepard is hoisted aboard a recovery helicopter, and gives a boost to President Kennedy's vow that America would be first to the moon.

from the man on the street was: "It's wonderful." But an Australian cattle rancher visiting New York City put it the way most people saw it—if incorrectly. "It was thrilling," he said. "Something the free world has been waiting for for several years. Now you've caught up with the people from Russia, and I hope you pass them."

The United States had not caught up, not yet. German rocket expert Wernher von Braun, whose team had given his new country its two singular space successes, said: "Only a humble beginning with greater things to come." Said President Kennedy, "All America rejoices in this successful flight . . . This is an historic milestone in our own exploration into space. But America still needs to work with the utmost speed and vigor in the further development of our space program."

Congratulations came from every major capital in the free world. In Europe, headlines proclaimed, "He's Up There! . . . Up And Down Alive!" Said one Britisher, "It

was a great privilege to be allowed to participate in Shepard's flight. I was pretty well up there in the capsule with him. The Americans had the right way of doing it . . . They allowed us all to take part in his fantastic adventure."

The Russian people heard the news an hour and a half after the fact. A female announcer said flatly, "According to information received from Cape Canaveral, a rocket with a man on board was launched. After 15 minutes the capsule with the pilot, Alan Shepard, fell in the Atlantic Ocean . . . Pilot Alan Shepard feels satisfactorily . . ."

Soviet Premier Nikita Khrushchev telegraphed congratulations in the name of the Soviet people. "The latest outstanding achievement in man's conquest of the cosmos opens up unlimited possibilities for the study of nature in the name of progress," he said. But earlier the same day in a speech in Armenia, he tended to pooh-pooh the limited nature of Shepard's flight compared with Gagarin's orbit. "Recently," he said, "with a mighty echo around the world, there was heard the news of triumphal flight of man in a cosmic ship all the way around the earth—and not just in one way or another." The official Soviet news agency, *Tass*, commented that Shepard's flight "cannot be compared with the flight of . . . Gagarin." On Grand Bahama Island for two days of rest and debriefing, Shepard tended to agree. "The only complaint I have," he said, "is that the flight wasn't long enough."

The national reaction to Shepard's flight was reflected in Congress, and in the advisory circles around the President. If critics were not silenced, they were at least momentarily cowed. The gloom of the Bay of Pigs, the frustrations of other confrontations, seemed to have melted away in the glow of the Shepard success.

Vice President Johnson, after submitting the tentative report on April 28, called on space agency chief Webb and Defense Secretary Robert McNamara and others for a final, detailed report on America's space future by May 8, the deadline created by the Vice President's impending goodwill tour to Southeast Asia, a tour that would bring him to another troubled nation called Vietnam. He received the report on deadline and submitted it to the President with a simple cover letter. It came on the same day that Shepard and the six other Mercury astronauts were welcomed by a quarter of a million people in a Washington motorcade and Shepard received a medal at a White House ceremony.

On the green lawn beside the Rose Garden, Kennedy made a short speech, after which he accidentally dropped the space agency's Distinguished Service Medal he was to award Shepard. Webb retrieved it and handed it to him. Kennedy quipped, "This decoration has gone from the ground up." He stood there with the others laughing until a nudge from his wife reminded him he had not yet pinned it on Shepard—which he did forthwith.

Then the President, the Vice President and the astronauts walked past the swelling green rose bushes, not yet in bloom, to the presidential office. Kennedy sat in his rocking chair, the Vice President beside him, and motioned to the astronauts who filled the two oyster white sofas on either side of the round coffee table. For 15 minutes, behind closed doors, they talked of the future of the space program.

So had the events of these days, combined with the reports he received earlier, convinced and involved Kennedy. So had they convinced and involved the nation. On May 25, Kennedy stood before a joint session of the Congress to deliver what amounted to a second State of the Union speech—this one entitled "Urgent National Needs."

It covered many subjects, from disarmament to social progress—and it dealt with space.

"Now is the time to take longer strides—time for a great new American enterprise —time for this nation to take a clearly leading role in space achievement, which in many ways may hold the key to our future on earth.

"I believe we possess all the resources and talents necessary. But the facts of the matter are that we have never made the national decision or marshalled the national resources required for such leadership. We have never specified long range goals on an urgent time schedule, or managed our resources and our time so as to insure their fulfillment.

"Recognizing the head start obtained by the Soviets with their large rocket engines . . . and recognizing the likelihood that they will exploit this lead for some time to come in still more impressive successes, we nevertheless are required to make new efforts on our own. For while we cannot guarantee that we shall one day be first, we can guarantee that any failure to make this effort will make us last. We take an additional risk by making it in full view of the world, but as shown by the feat of astronaut Shepard, this very risk enhances our stature when we are successful . . .

"I believe this nation should commit itself to achieving the goal, before the decade is out, of landing a man on the moon and returning him safely to earth. No single space project in this period will be more impressive to mankind, or more important for the long-range exploration of space; and none will be so difficult or expensive to accomplish."

So in 1961 did the nation commit itself to the challenge of space. Of all the modern challenges facing America, perhaps none had been so long ignored. The years that led to this year of decision were full of ironies, centering on one awful irony: America emerged from World War II as a technological giant; it seemed able to do anything it wanted to do. It concentrated on building an easy life. It awoke in 1957 to find its pride and prowess challenged by a Soviet Sputnik asail on a new ocean—space.

A Medal For Shepard—A grateful President pins it on as Virgil Grissom, John Glenn, Gordon Cooper, James Webb, the Vice President and Scott Carpenter stand by, all to play a part in forging America's space effort.

# 2 Victory—Stored In A Garage

In Huntsville, Ala., it was an otherwise ordinary October day in 1957. But, for the former German scientists and the Army officers of the Redstone Arsenal, it was more than that.

For over three years now they had pleaded with Eisenhower administration defense officials for permission to launch a satellite into space. For over a year they knew they had the rocket power to do it. But they were denied that permission.

At noon this overcast, warm autumn day, they received a party of Very Important Persons. The centerpiece of the group was the man who in the next week would take over as the new Secretary of Defense, Neil McElroy. He would succeed the controversial former head of General Motors Corp., Charles E. Wilson. The Huntsville team, especially chief rocket scientist Wernher von Braun and the commanding officer, Maj. Gen. John Bruce Medaris, hoped to convince McElroy of what they had failed repeatedly to convince Wilson—that they be given a satellite go-ahead. They felt the need was urgent.

Four months earlier, the Soviet Union had announced the radio channels it would use for earth satellites. Seven weeks earlier, the Soviets had fired a missile with power enough to reach from one continent to another. Clearly, they had the power to fire a sizable satellite into space. Clearly, they intended to use it soon.

The only U.S. space program, meanwhile, was a faltering, low priority, troubled plan—Project Vanguard—to launch a series of small satellites during the International Geophysical Year. It was months away from even a try.

McElroy's visit gave the Army experts another chance. They beset him with charts and figures, arguments and plans. The day ended with a cocktail and dinner party in a converted 100-year-old farmhouse on the Arsenal grounds. The VIP house was named appropriately "Goddard House," after American rocket pioneer Robert H. Goddard, a man who scraped together personal savings and donations from people like Charles A. Lindbergh to build and fire rockets in the 1920s. As evening fell, the cocktail party with a purpose got under way.

Von Braun and Medaris pressed their arguments with McElroy, answered his questions. Then with the ringing of a telephone came the news that made their arguments academic. Medaris' public information officer, Gordon Harris, at his Huntsville home, received a call from a London newspaper. The Soviet Union had launched a satellite they called Sputnik. Harris flashed the available details to the Arsenal party. Von Braun made some quick calculations and came up with an estimate on the size of the Soviet booster rocket that had shot the satellite into space. Then he turned excitedly on McElroy. Medaris, in his book *Countdown For Decision,* described his often-frustrated friend now overflowing with words.

"We knew they were going to do it!" Von Braun said. "Vanguard will never make it. We have the hardware on the shelf. For God's sake, turn us loose and let us do something. We can put up a satellite in 60 days, Mr. McElroy! Just give us a green light and 60 days!"

Medaris says he tried to calm his keyed-up expert with caution. "No, Wernher," he said. "Ninety days."

By now the entire cocktail party exploded into demands that the Army be given a chance, charges that they could have beaten the Russians. All of the frustrations of the past three years, and before, descended on McElroy that night.

What an odd mixture of motives there are in the affairs of men; the dreams of some, the ambition of others, all dependent on the power of a few. Any decision that brings satisfaction to one brings frustration to another.

To understand completely, it is necessary to reach back to the moods and events that swept America in the years following World War II. There were other ignored challenges, deeper ironies of motive and reason, that led to this bitter day in October in 1957.

The frustrations actually dated from World War II. Von Braun, Dr. Kurt Debus, Dr. Ernst Stuhlinger, and over 100 others worked on rocket research for the German Army at Pennemunde during the war. They designed and built the V-2 rocket for Hitler. In the war's final stages they fled the advancing Russians and turned themselves over to the U.S. Army which captured as well some 300 boxcar-loads of V-2 rockets and parts. Men and machines were sent to the United States in what was known as Operation Paperclip. It so aggravated Stalin that he is reported to have said, "This is absolutely intolerable. We defeated the Nazi armies; we occupied Berlin and Peenemunde; but the Americans got the rocket engineers." The Soviets captured a few top men and several hundred lower echelon technicians.

After the war, the United States was in no mood for armaments. It was in the mood for new cars and refrigerators and washing machines after five years of not having them. As Von Braun would later recall: "The United States had no ballistic missile program worth mentioning between 1945 and 1951. Those six years during which the Russians obviously laid the groundwork for their large rocket program are irretrievably lost . . . Our present dilemma is not due to the fact that we are not working hard enough now, but that we did not work hard enough during the first six to 10 years after the war."

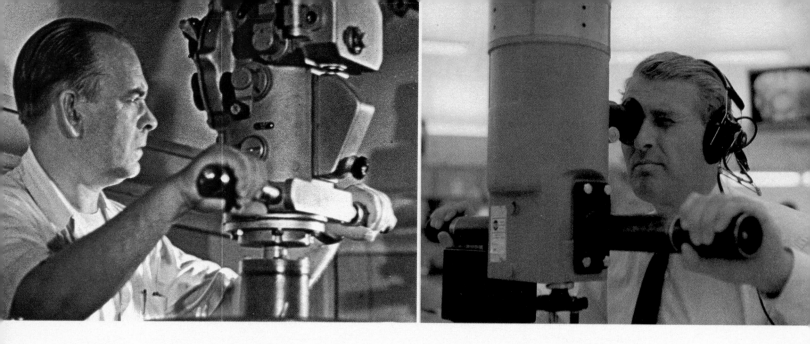

The Army put the German experts to work on a number of rocket and training projects. The Germans eventually became U.S. citizens and turned their talents to Army missile projects at the Redstone Arsenal. There they built the Redstone, a 200-mile range missile.

In those postwar years the Truman administration was shaken by two Communist affronts: the explosion of the first Soviet atomic weapon, and the war in Korea. Both events stimulated increased weapons spending, and some modest funding for both Army and Air Force rocket projects. The rapid development of hydrogen bombs, first by the United States, then by the Soviet Union, stimulated more spending for long-range missiles. Both the Army and the Air Force vied for dominance in the missile field. The rivalry between them was bitter.

The Eisenhower administration, in moderating this battle between the services, gave missile development top priority. When the idea of space satellites came up, it decided not to let this scientific exercise get in the way of the nation's crucial missile race. The line was drawn on July 29, 1955, when President Eisenhower announced that the Naval Research Laboratory would launch a number of grapefruit-sized satellites during the International Geophysical Year. The satellites, meant solely for scientific investigation, and the rockets that would launch them, were called Project Vanguard. The Eisenhower decision effectively separated the satellite program from the military power that could have put it in orbit. In so doing, the President rejected a Von Braun plan for satellite launchings, and deliberately isolated the U.S. space effort from the top priority military missile programs.

The day after the Eisenhower declaration, the Soviets announced that they too planned to launch earth satellites during IGY, and pointedly added that theirs would be bigger by far than the puny craft planned by the United States. The Russians, with their postwar head start, played a bolder game: their military missiles would be available to launch their scientific satellites.

To Von Braun and his cohorts, for years dreaming of space travel and trips to the moon, the U.S. separation of effort seemed wasteful and meaningless. Rocket power was rocket power, and it was needed to get into space. In 1956, in a test of a funny-

Not So Different—A Soviet launch commander views his fuming rocket through a periscope (left). Wernher von Braun does the same in an American blockhouse in the first primitive days of Sputniks and Explorers.

looking Rube Goldberg–type rocket, they knew they had what they needed—a full year before Sputnik went into orbit.

The test came in September of that year. The scientists elongated their basic Redstone rocket and put 10 small powder-filled rockets on top. They built this contraption for distance-firing, so that eventually they could test nose-cone designs with it. But first they had to see if it would work. The idea was for the stretched Redstone to push the small rocket cluster into near space, then fall away. The rocket clusters would then fire, driving a dummy warhead far out over the Atlantic. Because the rocket clusters were unstable, the scientists placed them in a sort of spinning bucket on top of the Redstone. The spin, like the spin of a bullet, would keep the course straight. This Redstone with a spinning bucket was called a Jupiter-C.

Then on September 20, 1956, they fired Missile 27, a Jupiter-C, from Cape Canaveral. It roared 3,000 miles out over the Atlantic and reached a peak height of 600 miles. By adding powder instead of sand in the warhead, they could have put it into orbit. They asked for permission to try. They were told to stick to building missiles.

So they took the backup missile, No. 29, and stored it in a garage-like shed where it waited for the minds of men to change.

And that is where Missile 29 remained, a self-denied answer to the Soviet challenge, even to this October day when, with Vanguard still having its troubles, the Army experts pressed Secretary of Defense-designate McElroy at the cocktail party in Huntsville.

Now on October 4, 1957, the Army rocket experts were sure that Sputnik would do what their arguments failed to do. So even though they did not have authorization to launch a satellite, they hauled Missile No. 29 out of the garage, blew away the dust and cobwebs and set to work. Surely, they thought, they'd get the go-ahead any day now.

No one could predict the shock that Sputnik I delivered to America. Even some of the men who would later chart America's way to the moon did not see it then. One, Christopher Columbus Kraft Jr., recalled, "I was a flight test engineer. I thought— well, they did it. But so what? . . . I wasn't aware it would have such an impact on the American people and our status as a nation technically. I think the people were right. And I was wrong."

Sputnik I burst on a perfect setting. It was a clear, sunny day in Washington. All day top U.S. scientists met with their Soviet counterparts on how they would cooperate in the International Geophysical Year. The atmosphere was warm and friendly. Out of curiosity, some of the Americans discreetly asked the Russians when they would launch their IGY satellite. Finally, in one open meeting, a top Russian

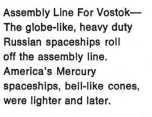

Assembly Line For Vostok— The globe-like, heavy duty Russian spaceships roll off the assembly line. America's Mercury spaceships, bell-like cones, were lighter and later.

apparently bridled at the question. "We do not brag about what we are going to do," he said. "We do it, and then we tell everything." Otherwise, recalls Dr. Homer Newell, now with the U.S. space agency, "the Soviets just played it with poker faces all day long."

That night, while Von Braun and Medaris hosted McElroy in Huntsville, the Soviet Embassy hosted U.S. scientists in Washington. The cocktail party on the Embassy's second floor had been under way about an hour when a newsman was informed of *The Associated Press* dispatch from Moscow. He quietly but quickly passed the word to senior U.S. scientists. One of them, Dr. Lloyd Berkner, called for silence. Then he announced the orbit of Sputnik I, and added, "I wish to congratulate our Soviet colleagues on their achievement." Some of the lower echelon Soviet scientists were as stunned and silent for the moment as their American guests. Then the Americans began shaking hands and congratulating the Soviets. Newsmen ran down the semicircular staircase for the telephones on the first floor. Within minutes, the party dissolved.

Some American scientists congregated that night at the National Academy of Sciences and from radio sightings plotted Sputnik's course over the earth long before the Soviets gave out the information. It was, at best, a vicarious thrill.

The White House was determined to keep a calm posture. Presidential news secretary James Hagerty, following the President's dictum, said, "We never thought of our satellite program as one which was in a race with the Soviets. Ours is geared to the IGY and is proceeding satisfactorily in accordance with its scientific objectives."

Senators and congressmen from both sides of the aisle had little patience with that explanation. Sputnik evoked statements such as these:

Adlai Stevenson, the Democrat who ran unsuccessfully against Eisenhower: "I hope our government will not be content with further misleading reassurances. I see nothing wrong with acknowledging Russia's accomplishment, but I see a great deal wrong with kidding ourselves. Not just our pride, but our national security is at stake."

Sen. Styles Bridges (R-N.H.): "The time has clearly come to be less concerned with the depth of pile on the new broadloom rug or the height of the tail fin on the new car and to be more prepared to shed blood, sweat and tears if this country and the free world are to survive."

But meantime, U.S. prestige was taking a beating overseas. The free world was just as shocked as the Americans were. And at home there were voices suggesting wholesale reappraisals of education, support for science, everything from the age Johnny begins math to the shortage of Ph.Ds. Such was the effect of the little radio station in space beeping out messages few could understand.

President Eisenhower congratulated the Soviet Union on October 9 and again explained the separation of military missile programs and the scientific satellite; again insisted, "Our satellite program has never been conducted as a race with other nations." At a news conference later, he said that Sputnik did not worry him, "not one

"There's Life Up There"—
The world would never be
the same. The first living
creature into orbit, Laika,
tested the effects of weightlessness, a sacrifice to pave
the way for men.

iota. Apparently from what they say," he added, "they have put one small ball in the air."

But Bernard Baruch, sage financier and counselor to presidents, wrote in the New York *Herald Tribune* on October 16, "If America ever crashes, it will be in a two-tone convertible. While we devote our industrial and technological power to producing new model automobiles and more gadgets, the Soviet Union is conquering space. America is worried. It should be. . . . Still there is no reason to panic. What human folly commits, human ingenuity can overcome . . . Sputnik is more than a satellite hurtling through space, more than a warning of leadership jeopardized and security imperiled. Sputnik represents a test of democracy. Do we meet this challenge—regain our leadership, assure our security? Do we discipline ourselves to protect our freedoms? If we do not, we will bear the far harsher disciplines which our enemies will impose on us."

To punctuate their superiority, on November 3, the Soviets fired Sputnik II into orbit—more than six times heavier than Sputnik I and carrying a dog named Laika. It was a sacrifice to answer the medical question whether living creatures can endure launch and weightless flight. Laika died in space and burned with Sputnik II when it fell to earth on April 14, 1958.

In the Senate, Majority Leader Lyndon B. Johnson (D-Tex.) began an investigation into U.S. space progress as chairman of the Senate Preparedness Committee. In response to the Sputniks he said, "This does not mean that we cannot catch up with the Soviet Union. It does mean that we have not kept in step with the needs of our times. The question of who is to blame is far less important than the question of what should be done."

But men always seek to fix blame. The most prophetic political statement came from former Sen. William Benton, a Connecticut Democrat. "I foretell," he said, "that these tragic blunders of the administration will show up in elections of 1958 and 1960." They did.

"It Was Sickening"—Chris Kraft recalls hearing the news of Vanguard's failure in a taxi in Washington, remembers it as the most disastrous day in the history of American space flights.

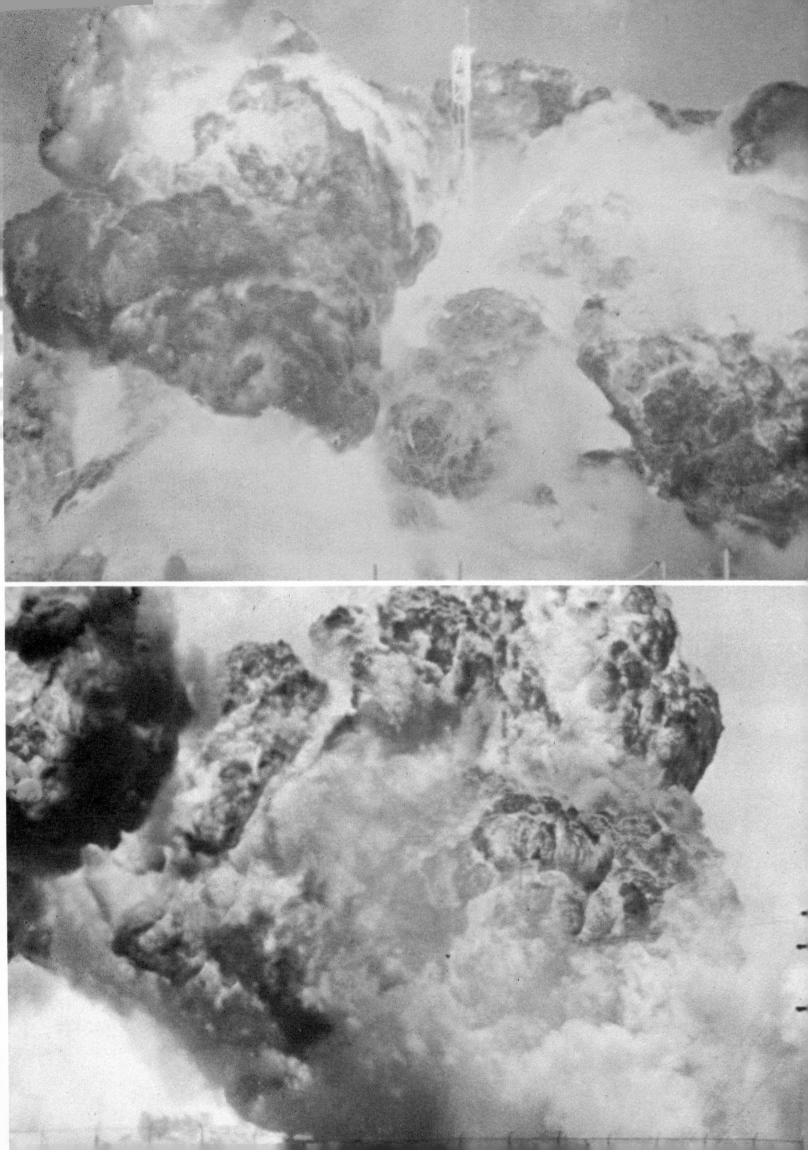

In the face of the national and world reaction, the Eisenhower administration began a slow and cautious reappraisal of the space race it continued to say didn't exist. Finally, on November 8, 1957, the men at Huntsville got the word: go ahead with Missile 29. Now they set to work in earnest, aiming for a January launch date.

Meanwhile, the Vanguard people, feeling the pressure of Sputnik as well, set themselves for a first test of their slender, trouble-plagued, three-stage rocket. It was only a test, they emphasized. But if it was totally successful, it would put a tiny satellite in orbit. There was, they repeated, only an outside chance of this. Public interest was running high, and on Friday, December 6, 1957, world attention focused on the Navy launch pad at Cape Canaveral.

The countdown reached zero. The rocket seemed to rise slightly. Then with a roar it collapsed on itself in a blossom of orange and yellow flame. And with it collapsed any hope of a quick recovery from the sting of Sputnik. The smoke that lingered over the Cape seemed to cover America. Chris Kraft, the man who felt "so what?" when Sputnik was launched, heard the news of the Vanguard failure while riding in a Washington taxi.

"I think that was a more disastrous day in the history of American space flights than any other day," he said. "It was sickening. It was very much doom and gloom as to what America's capabilities were. And that was before I was in the space program."

He was not alone. Test or not, America wanted a success, a balm for her pride.

The Vanguard failure and the reaction to it had shaken official Washington. When the Army shipped their Jupiter-C rocket to the Cape in January, orders were to keep the utmost secrecy. The gantry and the launch pad were covered with canvas shrouds to hide the rocket from the binoculars of newsmen now stationed permanently on the sands to the south. Harris was allowed to prepare a one-page release, but he was told to hold it. Launch date was scheduled for January 29, 1958. The Redstone crews worked feverishly, checking every detail.

Cape Canaveral was a remote base. There was little air travel. Most visitors arrived by train. Von Braun arrived on January 28, only to discover he would not be allowed to see his dreamchild launched. He was to be in Washington instead where the National Academy of Sciences would hold a news conference when and if the satellite went into orbit. The satellite carried the same radiation-sensing gear that was to have flown in Vanguard. The scientists would answer questions about that. Von Braun would answer for the rocket. It was too much for the rocket expert after all these years, all these dreams. He put up an argument. Medaris finally had to give him a direct order. Von Braun went to Washington.

The work on the Jupiter-C rocket went smoothly. But on the 28th, the day before the scheduled Wednesday launch, there was bad news. The jet stream, that river of high altitude air that governs much of the earth's weather, had shifted southward. It was roaring thousands of feet over the Cape at speeds up to 200 miles an hour. The broadside shearing force would tear a climbing rocket to bits.

Each day the Army team had to proceed as if a launch were possible. Each day the jet stream would make their efforts futile. There was little sleep. What there was came at odd hours. The Patrick Air Force Base weathermen kept sending up their balloons. Their answer was always the same. The future looked grim. The rocket men were unwilling to press their crews into the weekend because fatigue was already showing. Tension was high. The 29th passed. The 30th. More weather balloons. More wind.

Maj. Gen. Donald Yates, commanding officer of the base and the test range, had been one of Eisenhower's weather specialists on D-Day. He commiserated with the plight of the Jupiter-C team, but his own forecast was for no immediate relief from the jet stream. To make matters worse, the Army was running out of its allotted time on the range.

Finally, on one of the calls to Patrick, the Army people reached a young Air Force lieutenant; no one remembers his name now. He said he thought the winds might abate during the night of the 30th. His general, he said, might not agree with him, but that was his forecast, and he wasn't planning on making the Air Force a career anyway. The rocket men ran the new figures through the computer at Huntsville. If the prediction was right, they would launch on the night of Friday, January 31.

The balloons confirmed the lieutenant's guess the next morning. The countdown proceeded on Missile 29 and its slender, pencil-shaped satellite—31 pounds of metal and instruments. The afternoon passed. The night wore on.

In the blockhouse, the Army experts under Dr. Kurt Debus watched through the heavy safety glass windows at the work on the pad. There were small problems. A

Out Of The Garage—The German scientists pulled out their Jupiter-C rocket, a weird contraption with a spinning bucket on top. It put America's first satellite, Explorer I, into orbit, and helped salvage the nation's pride.

radar went out; a fuel line leaked. But all problems were overcome. The launch pad was cleared. The gantry was pulled back. The rocket stood alone, gleaming white in the glare of searchlights. The blockhouse crew ran through the final checklists, listening to the confirming voices on their headsets.

At zero-minus-12 minutes, the bucket containing the upper stage rockets began to spin. The minutes ticked away. Then a key was turned. The final automatic 20 seconds began. "Firing command . . . Main stage . . . Ignition! Liftoff!" The rocket climbed slowly off the pad, seeming to stand on its own tail of fire, gathering speed, pushing toward space.

The blockhouse rang with cheers and cries of "Go, baby, go." Some distance away, in a building used by the Army team, Dr. Ernst Stuhlinger had no time to cheer. Using a special sliderule he devised, he was checking the figures from the blockhouse, as the Jupiter-C rose over the Atlantic and reached for the edge of space. When the main stage fell away, he had to calculate to the second the time to fire the second stage rockets by a radioed command. The third and fourth stages would fire automatically. Gordon Harris, the public information officer, was sitting on a stool in the blockhouse. He had been warned to speak softly and keep cool, as he reported to newsmen over an open telephone line. He kept saying, "It looks good . . . Still looks good."

The first tracking stations reported contact with the rocket, but to be sure they had orbit, the Army men had decided to wait until it came around the other side of earth and was picked up by the Jet Propulsion Laboratory's big radio antenna at Goldstone, Calif. In Washington, officials waited for word so that the President could announce America's first satellite. In his book, Medaris says he received a message from Secretary of the Army Wilbur Brucker that said, "I'm out of coffee and we are running out of cigarettes. What do I do now?" Medaris says he answered, "Send out for more and sweat it out with the rest of us."

The rocket was late. All the radio information from the range looked good. But the fact remained that the rocket was late. Was it in orbit? Medaris and others went to a midnight news conference at the Patrick Air Force Base post theater. They told the newsmen all they knew. It looked good. Still no confirmation of orbit. Then someone passed a slip of paper to Medaris. He read it with tired eyes, and his face lit up in a second. It said only four words, "Goldstone has the bird." Brucker telephoned from Washington to give the bird its official name—it had none until then. "Call it Explorer," he said.

Explorer was in orbit, and so was America, at last.

In the small hours of the morning when they finally returned to their motel well south of the Cape area, a figure came out of darkness and grabbed Medaris around the middle, lifting him off the ground. It was the motel owner. He put the general down and began pumping his hand, overflowing with congratulations. He reflected the mood of the nation. After a couple of hours sleep, Medaris returned to Huntsville and the second birthday celebration of the Army Ballistic Missile Agency. He was greeted by

At Last—Vanguard hurls its tiny package into space, a ball-like satellite that would circle the globe for hundreds of years.

headlines in the *Huntsville Times* that screamed, "Jupiter-C Puts Up Moon . . . Eisenhower Officially Announces Huntsville Satellite Circles Globe." The edition of the paper was called "Satellite Extra."

In the coming weeks, the radio reports from Explorer's sensors indicated the great belts of radiation that ring the world. They were christened the Van Allen belts after the man who had conceived and built the experiment, Dr. James A. Van Allen of the University of Iowa. But as important as the scientific discovery was, it could not match the emotional and political impact of the first U.S. satellite. It put America back in the space race, whether anyone admitted one existed or not.

A February try with Vanguard failed. A March attempt to orbit another Explorer failed. Then, with the pressure off, the Vanguard people scored their first success on March 17. They hurled the tiny Vanguard into an orbit that would last between 200 and 1,000 years. Radio tracking of the little moon indicated that the earth was not a perfect sphere. As suspected, it had a slight southern bulge, a tendency toward pear-shape, but hardly enough to notice. Explorer III followed in a few days, but the Russians showed how puny the American rocket power was. In May they hurled the 3,000-pound Sputnik III into orbit. That one satellite outweighed all the U.S. satellites to date, 56-to-1.

There were important changes brewing in Washington. The United States had a space effort now, but too many houses to put it in. The Army, the Air Force and the Navy were all firing unmanned satellites into space at an accelerating pace. The Air Force began to think in terms of putting a man up—a project they called Man In Space Soonest, or MISS. The Army proposed Project Adam—the launching of a man on a simple looping flight into the Atlantic, about as technically useful, said one scientist, "as the circus stunt of shooting a young lady from a cannon." The Navy proposed something called Manned Earth Reconnaissance, or MER. It was expensive and required completely new rocket systems. The Army proposal was considered not ambitious enough. The Air Force plan received serious study.

One of the most respected agencies in the aeronautic field, with only a fringe effort in space, was beginning to stir as well. It was the National Advisory Committee for Aeronautics. More than a committee, it was a series of research facilities that provided other government bodies like the Air Force with the fruits of its elemental research.

Sputnik caught NACA just before what it called its annual inspection—a review of NACA research on such aeronautical areas as supersonic flight, transonic flight, thrust reversers and so on. The meeting was scheduled for October 8 at NACA's Lewis Air Research Center at the Cleveland airport. Four days before the open meeting, Sputnik orbited the earth. Suddenly, space was "in." As one old NACA hand recalled, in two days he had to completely change the accent of the meeting, redo charts, everything to "put us into research in the space business . . . It wasn't by any means a dishonest thing we did. It was just—accentuate the positive."

In the days following Sputnik, there were meetings at almost every level of NACA to chart the future of the organization in space. Its rank and file people were clearly aeronautical in accent. For that matter, there were few people in the world who specialized in space technology then. Still, NACA had some who had stepped up their thinking from the air to the vacuum of space. Among them was Maxime Faget, 37, a former Navy submariner. His father, a doctor, helped develop sulfone drugs for the treatment of leprosy. Faget himself was to become a prime designer in the techniques of manned space flight.

Politically, NACA stood by its role as research adviser, while the Air Force, the Army and the Navy pressed for manned flight money the Eisenhower administration was unwilling to give. The Eisenhower position remained that space should be a purely scientific arena. In a letter to Soviet Premier Nikolai Bulganin in early 1958 the President asked, "Should not outer space be dedicated to the peaceful uses of mankind and denied to the purposes of war?"

While the military services encountered only frustration for their man-in-space plans, a number of suggestions were on the table for a civilian space agency. In January 1958, Lyndon Johnson presented the findings of his Senate Preparedness Investigating Committee calling for the establishment of an independent space agency. In April, President Eisenhower sent the Democratic-controlled Congress a bill to create a civilian space agency. Under the guidance of Sen. Johnson, Congress in July created the National Aeronautics and Space Administration to carry out U.S. space assignments, and a National Aeronautics and Space Council to advise the President. Eisenhower signed the bill into law July 29, and named T. Keith Glennan, president of Case Institute of Technology, the first NASA administrator, and Hugh Dryden, NACA director, as his deputy.

The conversion was officially set for October 1, 1958. It brought most of America's space effort under one roof. Overnight, some 8,000 NACA employes had a new employer, and a new purpose. On the same day, William C. Schneider, then a Navy missile expert and later to guide two-man Gemini space flights and the post-Apollo program, was attending a technical symposium at an NACA center. "I marveled that the night before the signs all said NACA," he said, "and in the morning when we went there all the signs said NASA."

Ultimately, the Naval Research Laboratory's Vanguard experts and the Army's Redstone experts who had launched the first two American satellites were brought into NASA. Defense budget money for space also went to NASA. At about the same time, the space agency was given the role of putting American astronauts into space. It congregated 25 top-flight engineers from the Lewis and Langley centers at Langley and called them the Space Task Group, the forerunner of the Manned Spaceflight organization. At the planning meeting for the manned space effort, administrator Glennan concluded the discussion with the words, "All right. Let's get started."

In retrospect, Eisenhower aide Sherman Adams looked back on the attitudes of Congress, the President, and himself in those pre- and post-Sputnik days.

"The high costs of missile development and space rocketry had greatly hampered research in those fields until Sputnik I came along," he said. "Then Congress, with the national pride at stake, could not spend money fast enough in its eagerness to beat the Soviets to the moon. Until that time, nobody in Washington had really given much consideration to the possible importance of an invasion of space as psychological propaganda or even as scientific achievement. There were too many other critical emergencies.

"But when Sputnik was launched," he went on, "the same congressmen who had been cutting funds for scientific research a few years earlier came to the President begging him to make a strong statement that would restore the people's trust and confidence. Eisenhower said he preferred to play down the whole thing.

"I was asked what I thought about it and I made a widely-quoted remark about the administration not being intent on attaining a high score in any outer space basketball game. I was only trying to reflect the President's desire for calm poise, but I had to admit on reflection that my observation seemed to be an over-emphasis on de-emphasis."

Meanwhile, in those last years of the Eisenhower administration, the United States continued to make progress in the launching of both scientific and military satellites. In December 1958 the United States launched an Atlas missile into orbit with no scientific purpose. It carried a tape-recorded Christmas message from President Eisenhower and broadcast it to the world. It was a dramatic and public demonstration of the weight-lifting capacity of the Atlas rocket which was the nation's first intercontinental ballistic missile. But as a satellite, it was little more than an empty rocket, weighing 8,750 pounds, the heaviest in space to that date. The supersecret shot was named appropriately Project Score.

As the decade ended, the Soviet Union had successfully probed the moon and orbited living creatures, recovering them from space. The United States scientific satellites had discovered remarkable mysteries about the earth and the shell of power around it. The United States had also orbited weather satellites, communications satellites, navigation satellites, Echo balloon satellites and spy satellites. The Air Force learned how to drop containers from orbiting satellites and catch them in mid-air. The space age was moving into a new and sophisticated era.

But before the decade ended, there was a sad note to U.S. space affairs. Robert H. Goddard, the remarkable American who invented and tested rocket systems in the 1920s and whose work inspired rocket men all over the world, died in August 1945.

On August 5, 1960, the space agency and the Department of Defense settled a patent infringement claim with his estate, a claim that had been pending since 1951. The amount was $1 million. At the same time, the Smithsonian Institution awarded Goddard its Langley Medal posthumously, thus adding his name to a list that begins with the Wright brothers, includes Charles Lindbergh, Gustave Eiffel and Richard E. Byrd, and finally, 15 years after his death, Robert H. Goddard, the father of American rocketry.

# 3 Men, Machines And Monkeys

First they were going to call it Project Astronaut. But they decided that would put too great a focus on the personality of the man. When all the suggestions were in, and the arguments over, they chose Project Mercury. That was the name they gave to the first U.S. man-in-space program—harkening to the fleet messenger of the gods, winged sandals, winged helmet, the son of Zeus, the grandson of Atlas. They announced it on Wright Brothers Day, December 17, 1958. A little more than half a century after Americans first leapt into the air, it became their stated purpose to leap into space.

The assignment for putting Americans into space had been given to the civilian space agency by presidential decision more than a month before the agency came into existence. It tackled that ambitious goal before it had a real chance to get organized.

"That would have been the tidy, orderly way of doing it," remembers one early member of the space team. "But here we were, trying to run at a gallop when we hadn't even gotten out of the crib."

So it was in the late months of 1958 as the newly gathered experts began to put together the requirements for the machines of Project Mercury. At the same time they set the criteria for the men, yet to be chosen, who would fly the machines yet to be built.

One early decision was crucial. Men would have a role in flying. They would not be mere passengers at the mercy of an automatic pilot. Since the craft would be experimental and every tiny detail of its behavior would have to be noted, the first spacemen would have to be experienced test pilots as well. They would need to be volunteers with college degrees. They would have to be between the ages of 25 and 40. Because of spacecraft limitations they could be no more than 5-feet-11-inches tall. They would have to be in perfect physical condition.

President Eisenhower decided they would best come from the military services. The Army had no graduate test pilots, so the early screening list included 58 Air Force test pilots, 47 from the Navy, five from the Marines. Some were too tall. Some failed for other reasons. By March, 1959, the list was down to 32. Physically and psychologically, they probably were the most studied, examined men in history. Doctors probed and mapped each man in detail, learned everything there was to learn short of what surgery would tell, even down to the radiation count and the specific gravity of each body. In trying to whittle down the last 18, the space agency could get no lower than seven, one more than they wanted. Although they had set out to choose six, they accepted all seven.

One man close to the program noted there may have been another consideration at this time. It seemed more than coincidence that the final list included three from the Air Force, three from the Navy, and a Marine, about as even a division between the services as was possible.

They began their orientation and training at Langley Research Center. On April 9, 1959, they were helicoptered to Washington and introduced to the public at a news conference. Later, when the flights were under way, psychiatrists were asked what special elements the astronauts had in common. One of them smiled and said: "You know, we were talking about that the other day. And we discovered that they were almost all white, Anglo-Saxon Protestants from small midwestern towns with strong fathers. And the psychiatrists who helped choose them were almost all Jewish boys from New York City with strong mothers."

One element the psychiatrists did lay out—the astronauts and their wives showed strong individual independence; the kind of people who could form strong attachments for one another, but if necessary could say goodbye and start new lives. In the dangerous new arena of space, their meaning was grim.

Four of the astronauts were juniors, named after their fathers. The oldest was Lt. Col. John Herschel Glenn Jr. of the U.S. Marine Corps. The others were Air Force Capts. Donald K. Slayton, Leroy Gordon Cooper Jr. and Virgil I. Grissom, and, from the Navy, Lt. Cmdrs. Walter Marty Schirra Jr. and Alan Bartlett Shepard Jr., and Lt. Malcolm Scott Carpenter. They would become household names in America, those seven. Not all would survive, but among those who would there were fame and riches in store, not always in equal portion.

From the beginning there were dozens of firms willing to give them anything for the publicity—insurance, homes, cars. Most of it was turned down flatly. But few in the space agency expected the enormous public interest that would focus on these few men. The space agency's public information officer, Walter Bonney, recognized one thing that would have to be settled before it became a problem. He had seen what happened to other pioneers from the military services who had sold their personal stories. He was afraid it would happen to the astronauts.

"I could see it coming," he said. "That we'd have seven astronauts, each peddling his story to seven different magazines, or seven different publishers. Which would mean instead of working as a team, they'd all be jockeying for position. Because the man who made the first flight would be worth $100,000, and the rest of them would be worth $500. So I went over and saw (C.) Leo D'Orsey."

D'Orsey, a well-known Washington attorney, now deceased, was counsel for several celebrities including Arthur Godfrey, Edward R. Murrow and Bob Considine. He knew the legal aspects of a writer's income.

"And," said Bonney, "I said to him in so many words, 'Leo, I want you to do a public service that you won't get a dime for.' I told him what the problem was, and he said he'd help. He was tremendously excited and enthused about what the boys were going to be doing.

"So then I flew down to Langley, and talked to the astronauts. I said, 'Now look, you can do it any way you want. But this is what I think you ought to think in terms of.' They agreed."

D'Orsey briefed the astronauts on what they might expect. His estimates were conservative. Through his efforts they sold the magazine and book rights to their personal stories to Time-Life Inc. for half a million dollars, to be divided equally among them.

And while the public learned more about these heroes in waiting, a number of lesser heroes were paving the way for the humans who would follow them into space.

The Soviets almost always chose dogs when it came to testing stress and performance in space. The Americans used monkeys, chimpanzees, pigs, cats, rats, mice, rabbits, hamsters, even sea urchin eggs. But never a dog. In Russia the canine was a frequent medical research tool. But in America, a dog was a man's best friend, and a

Seven Against Space—A family portrait of America's first astronauts, chosen to blaze through the most dangerous test missions in the U.S. space program. From left, first row: Walter Schirra Jr., Donald Slayton, John Glenn, Scott Carpenter. Back row: Alan Shepard, Virgil Grissom, Gordon Cooper. One would never fly. One would perish. One would become the greatest American hero since Lindbergh.

Four-Inch Flight—"All we did was to launch the escape tower." The first test of Mercury-Redstone fails.

cold night was something you wouldn't send a dog into. And space is the coldest night of all.

The whole idea of sending up an animal was to see what man in a machine could withstand. It provided some of the most incongruous situations in which the U.S. government ever found itself. In the late 1950s, there were high speed centrifuge tests with chimpanzees, delivering pressures up to 40 times the pull of gravity in the interests of sparing humans harm. Researchers proving the Mercury spacecraft design also laid pigs on their backs strapped in small-scale astronaut couches, and dropped them in dummy spacecraft to see how well creatures with backbones could survive impacts in which they felt 58 times their own weight, for a fraction of a second. To everyone's delight, the pigs got up and slowly walked away.

The first living creatures launched from Cape Canaveral and recovered were two monkeys, a North American-born rhesus monkey named Able, and a South American-born squirrel monkey named Baker. They shared the same cabin on a trip 300 miles high and 1,500 miles out over the Atlantic at speeds up to 10,000 miles an hour. Preparations were "secret beyond secret."

Rocket men, flown in from Huntsville to prepare the missile, were lodged in military quarters so that their names wouldn't appear on local hotel registers. But no one warned the medical officers, down for their first launch. They marched into a local motel and signed in with rank, name, and M.D. The word raced around town that flight surgeons were on hand and there was a man in the missile. To put out the fire, officials confided there would be monkeys, not a man, on the flight, and asked newsmen to hold the information until the launch.

The mixed Army, Navy and Air Force team operated out of a hangar on the Cape. They had radio contact with Puerto Rico, which would then relay messages to the naval vessel that would pick up the monkeys when they splashed down. The only problem was that everything had to be in code, and the ship's radio had a range of barely 10 miles. "You wouldn't believe the sleazy way we operated then," said one Cape veteran. "Shoestrings."

After splashdown, the Cape launch team messaged, "Are the monkeys alive?" They couldn't reach the ship. It got later and later. Finally a detachment gathered at Patrick Air Force Base, south of the Cape, to ponder the problem. By now it was hours after the shot. The news that the monkeys had been launched was out. A nation starved for some sign of space progress waited. Gen. Yates, Patrick Air Force commandant, was surprised to see the worried faces when he arrived at the base at 5:30 a.m. "What's the problem?" he asked.

"The problem is that there's a room full of press out there waiting for us to tell them something," a launch team member said. "The White House is on the phone trying to find out. And we don't know. What the hell are we going to do?"

Yates tried in vain to reach the ship through his communications channels. One enterprising officer even tried commercial radio-telephone but could get no farther than Puerto Rico. Finally, in desperation, the team decided to ignore code and simply broadcast a message to the ship in the clear. The question flashed through the airwaves again, "Are the monkeys alive?" About half an hour later, the answer came back, "Yes, yes." That's all it said. So there was another big argument. What did that mean?

One official said, "Look, I can only conclude that if they said it twice it means both."

"Well," said another, "if we go in there and say both of them are alive, and one of them is dead, what then?"

"Well then," said the first, "the goddammed thing will just have to have died after we got the message."

Both monkeys were safe and sound aboard the ship, a fact corroborated about two hours later. Headlines and radios blared the news of the success. The squirrel monkey, Baker, was taken by its Navy handlers and bred through several generations without consequence. The Army's rhesus monkey, Able, was sent to Fort Knox where a civilian doctor had the job of removing the sensors that had recorded Able's life signs while he was in flight. "That's all he had to do," said one team member who recalled the flight. "And he killed it in the process. And so now the monkey is stuffed and in the Smithsonian."

Two small rhesus monkeys, Sam and Miss Sam, got short rocket rides late in 1959 and early in 1960. Both survived and helped show man could withstand the stresses of abrupt rocket power. But the animal that paved the way for Alan Shepard was the first real animal hero in the U.S. menagerie. The space agency established a colony of six trained chimpanzees behind its hangar area on the Cape. The chimps were trained to hit certain levers in response to flashing lights. If they did it correctly, they received

Ham Paves The Way—The chimpanzee, welcomed home as a hero, rode the Mercury-Redstone in a looping, 15-minute dash into space to set the stage for American astronauts. Banana pellets were his reward.

rewards of banana pellets. If they missed or ignored the lights, they received a mild shock to the sole of the foot as punishment.

The space agency was concerned about public reaction to the flight of a chimpanzee. If the animal were lost, it could arouse bad feelings, especially among animal lovers. If the chimp received much prior publicity, became a sort of personality, the ill effects would be heightened. There were a number of meetings on the subject, one of which concerned the name the first chimpanzee would carry into space. On official documents he was listed only as "Animal Subject 65." His real name was Chang. But space officials decided not to call him that for fear of arousing the wrath of "every Chinese laundryman in America." Finally they decided to call him Ham—after Holloman Aeromedical, the Air Force team that trained him.

It was a dress rehearsal for the Shepard flight, using the same kind of rocket, the same techniques. The recovery forces were spread out along the line of flight as they would be for a manned shot. Eight Navy ships, squads of amphibious tractors and tanks, flights of helicopters and Navy patrol planes stood by. On January 31, 1961, Ham boarded the Mercury spacecraft and was strapped into his little couch. After delays of some four hours he was shot on a looping flight to the edge of space and down again. A combination of malfunctions gave him a rougher ride than expected. He landed 422 miles downrange, about 150 miles beyond the target ship. When he splashed down he was all alone in the Atlantic. By the time helicopters found his bobbing spaceship, it was on its side and had taken on about 800 pounds of sea water. But Ham was safe, and in spite of the high gravity forces he endured during launch and descent, he performed his lever pulling tasks well. Aboard the recovery ship, he was given an apple as a reward. He was flown to Grand Bahama Island for a physical examination, and finally returned to a hero's welcome at Patrick Air Force Base. There were flashbulbs popping and cheers as he came down the airplane steps. "Ham was a baby chimp," recalls one who was there. "And they put little diapers on him, and a little jump suit, and he came down looking cute as heck."

A chimpanzee also paved the way for John Glenn's orbital flight. But a combination of errors forced flight officials to bring him down an orbit early. His name was Enos, chosen from the Greek and Hebrew because it meant "man." Enos was an import from the French Cameroons. Most of his backup chimps, Duane, Jim, Rocky and Ham, were recruited from circuses. Enos was bigger than Ham—and tougher. Like Ham, he had been trained to pull levers in answer to the colored lights. He was expert at it.

Enos was launched on a clear November day on an intended three orbits of the earth. The launch was perfect, but there was trouble ahead. One of the small jets that controlled the position of the spacecraft in orbit went dead. The automatic pilot, trying to correct for it, used up too much fuel. In addition, the lever system Enos was using went awry. One space agency official explained, "When he did the right thing, he got a shock. And finally he flipped his lid and tore the goddammed spacecraft apart. I don't blame him. They finally brought him back early. And then they took him to Grand Bahama Island, and then to Patrick Air Force Base.

Gus Grissom's Day—The Liberty Bell spaceship is hauled to the top of the Redstone rocket, and Grissom (right) suits up for his flight, America's second into space.

"I'm Just Going Along For The Ride."—Grissom blasts off on a hot July day, duplicates Shepard's flight, and splashes down in the Atlantic 15 minutes later. It was a soggy recovery and Grissom stepped from the recovery helicopter to get a thorough medical check and tell space agency experts about his five weightless minutes.

"Enos was not nasty beforehand," the official explained. "But if you had been trained to hit the right light for a reward, and you did and got a shock, well, you can imagine. At Patrick, there's a great press contingent outside, and they have it all roped off, all for this one chimp. Inside the plane, at the end of a very long aisle, there is the space hero. In a very large, strong cage."

It was suggested that the handlers bring Enos out for pictures. "Okay," said the medical officer, "let's get this over with." He told an Air Force sergeant to pick up Enos and bring him down the steps. The sergeant turned white.

"Enos, he don't take to being picked up," the sergeant said.

Nevertheless they opened the cage and brought Enos out, holding his arms outstretched so that their hands were away from Enos' angry teeth.

"I'll never forget," said one space veteran. "Everyone is waiting for the applause of the crowd for this little space hero. And this four-legged, hairy, ugly thing is walking all the way up the plane, and they bring him down the steps, and the handlers are smiling, and everybody is smiling, and Enos is showing his teeth, and it looks like he's smiling too. There was a marvelous picture in the newspapers the next day, and the headline said, 'Space Hero Enos—Happy After Space Flight.' And there was Enos' teeth showing. Stick out your hand and he'd bite it off."

The Soviets used dogs, singly and in pairs, to test out their spacecraft. Bred for generations afterwards, the dogs showed no ill effects of their flights. As a goodwill and propaganda gesture, the Soviets gave one of the offspring of their space dogs to President Johnson as a gift.

Besides successful animal flights, the way to Shepard's and Glenn's success was paved with dozens of launch pad disappointments, silly-looking misfires and spectacular explosions. On July 29, 1960, the two-year-old space agency readied for the first test of the Mercury spaceship on top of the powerful Atlas, an intercontinental ballistic rocket with a skin so thin you could hammer a hole in it, and power so fierce that its tail flame shot out the length of a football field. This was an unmanned test, and the giant rocket roared off the pad and disappeared into the rain clouds covering the Cape. Everything looked good. But after one minute all contact with the rocket was lost. Out of sight, it had exploded in a great orange and yellow fireball. It meant at least six months lost in the young space race.

Ironically, on this same day, the space agency announced a proposal called Project Apollo, a three-man spaceship with the ability to circle the earth for extended periods, or to fly around the moon. But Apollo was little more than an in-house idea, without funds and without contracts. Without presidential approval, it was to remain that way for almost a year.

Before Shepard could fly, space officials needed to know that the escape system in the rocket worked perfectly. On the face of it, the system looked simple. It was a group of rockets in a tower on top of the Mercury spacecraft. If something went wrong with the booster rocket below, the escape rockets would fire immediately and pull the spaceship and its astronaut to safety and an emergency landing in the sea. But one after another test of the escape system failed, almost down to the wire on the Shepard flight.

Launch experts also had to test the mating of the Redstone rocket and the spacecraft. On November 21, 1960, they were set to fire this combination without a man aboard. The countdown reached zero, the rocket ignited, wobbled slightly, and suddenly shut down, settling back on the launch pad. Then in a comedy of miscues the escape rocket blew. From the top of the Mercury capsule, like favors from a trick party hat, out came the drogue parachute, then the main parachute, then the reserve parachute, and it all unraveled and fluttered down around the rocket.

"All we did was to launch the escape tower," said a space agency official. Later, when they could laugh about it, they called it "the four-inch flight of Mercury-Redstone One." But to this day, Chris Kraft remembers the scene as "almost disastrous . . . That was a hell of a mess."

A month later, the system was tested successfully, and the space agency men learned to live in cycles of despair and triumph.

The Shepard flight vindicated the Mercury spacecraft and the Redstone rocket and gave America its first entry in the record books for manned space flight. Next came Virgil I. Grissom, a quiet, self-effacing man everyone called "Gus."

Thirty-five-years old, 5-feet-7, sparing of words, Gus Grissom discounted a comparison of the early Mercury flights to the first flights of the Wright brothers. The Wrights flew their machines, he said. "I'm just going along for the ride."

His flight would duplicate Shepard's—116 miles high, 302 miles out over the Atlantic. "I'm going to be scared," he admitted before the launch, "but I know it's going to work." He named his spaceship Liberty Bell.

After delays caused by weather, Grissom blasted off on July 21, 1961. Fellow astronaut Gordon Cooper, flying an F106 jet fighter, watched the launch from above, saw Liberty Bell disappear toward the edge of space. Grissom's remarks from space were technical, his spacecraft's attitude and condition. But toward the end of the flight, only 15 minutes long, he told the ground he had become too awed by the sight of the earth sweeping along below him and he had fallen behind in his chores.

He also thought he saw a star, and it would have been the first seen by any U.S. spaceman in the blackness above. His backup pilot, John Glenn, had bet Alan Shepard a steak dinner that he would see a star in the heavens. Shepard didn't. Grissom doubled the bet with Glenn, and for a while it looked like the red-headed Marine had won. But on checking it turned out to be a planet. Glenn lost again. America had much to learn about what could and could not be seen in the fabric of space. Later flights proved the eyes needed time to adjust to the contrast between the faint sources of pure light and the blackness around them.

But there was trouble ahead in an otherwise perfect flight. The spacecraft splashed down without incident. Helicopters came into view. Grissom asked for a few more minutes before he exited to complete some charts of his final instrument readings. "I was lying on my back, minding my own business," he said, "when pow! The next thing I knew I could see blue sky, and water coming over the sill."

What had happened was the premature explosion of bolts holding the emergency hatch closed. In seconds, Grissom struggled out of the cramped quarters in his now sinking spacecraft. His spacesuit was air-filled and waterproof. But there was trouble there, too. "I had neglected to close a port in the suit," Grissom said. "Water was coming into the suit and I was getting lower and lower. It was rather hard to stay afloat."

He tried to swim back to the waterlogged spacecraft to help the helicopters rescue it, but to no avail. Liberty Bell 7 sank in three-mile-deep waters. After some difficulty, caught in the downdraft from the helicopter rotors, he was finally picked up. He was standing on the deck of the USS Randolph, an aircraft carrier, 41 minutes after he had blasted off the pad at Cape Canaveral.

A few hours later, in Washington, President Kennedy signed a bill giving the space agency nearly $1.8 billion for the year ahead. The House and Senate had given him every cent he had asked for. It provided for a variety of space projects including a start on Project Apollo and the road to the moon.

"Once again we have demonstrated the technological excellence of this country," Kennedy said, something no one would have dared iterate a year earlier. "As our space program continues . . . it will continue to be this nation's policy to use space for the advancement of all mankind, and to make free release of all scientific and technological results."

Grissom's flight was hidden by the shadow of Shepard's pioneering mission, and it was all to be lost in the birth of a new American space hero seven months later. But in the end of the space program's early and middle years, few astronauts would make as great a contribution as Grissom and none would make a greater sacrifice.

# 4 The Magnificent Men...

America now had two astronauts who had braved the edge of space. But no American had yet flown into orbit. Yuri Gagarin's flight still stood as the only one that had circled the earth. And the Russians were not idle.

Less than three weeks after Grissom's waterlogged success, Gherman Titov, a Soviet major, shot into orbit from the Soviet base at Tyuratam. His Vostok II spaceship carried him 17 times around the globe. He took off on August 6 and parachuted to earth more than 25 hours later. His only problem in flight was a recurrent dizziness or vertigo, especially severe when he turned his head sharply or watched fast-moving objects flash by the spaceship window. To U.S. flight surgeons it raised a persistent question: would a human be able to endure long periods of weightlessness?

To the United States, a part of the space race for the first time, it was an appalling measure of the Soviet lead. Titov's endurance test eclipsed most of the future flight plans on the drawing boards of the Mercury team, and it came before there was any surety that the Americans could put a man into orbit at all. In fact, the space agency was still trying to prove out the Mercury spaceship in tandem with the only rocket available that had the power to put it in orbit, the Atlas. The last failure of the Mercury-Atlas system came in April, 1961. Finally there was a success in September. Then, in November, the chimpanzee Enos rode a lumbering Atlas into orbit around the earth twice, and finally the stage was set for a man.

The man would be John Glenn, the oldest astronaut, a careful man who had been backup pilot to both Shepard and Grissom, who had rehearsed those flights as his own.

Tentatively, the space agency set December, perhaps the 20th, for Glenn's orbital try. At Cape Canaveral, the technicians and engineers began the tortured, painstaking task of erecting and testing the rocket, the spacecraft. Behind all of their efforts was concern for the man who would fly into orbit, and concern with Gherman Titov, who had done it already.

"This, my friend, is a consciously competitive sport . . . This is not a tweedy, pipe-smoking atmosphere. We have no time to play with theories. . . . We have to find a balance between prudence and urgency," said one engineer.

A balance between prudence and urgency. They didn't make the December date. Now it would be January, 1962, the sixth year into the space race, the second year of manned flight.

On Launch Complex 14 at the Cape they set up the Atlas rocket No. 109D, a 93-foot monster with a shell so fragile it had to be pressurized or it would collapse on itself, barely more than a metal balloon, its skin thinner than a dime. Cost of the rocket alone: $2 million.

Above the rocket, they hoisted the Mercury spacecraft, mating the two with a metal girdle. They tested the joined systems, already tested separately a thousand times, a hundred times more. They pressed for as near precision as men can get. John Glenn named his craft Friendship 7. Cost of the spacecraft: $2.5 million.

And finally there was Glenn, balding, freckled, boyish-faced, a crack Marine pilot who downed three Communist MIGs in the last nine days of the Korean War, who won five Distinguished Flying Crosses and 18 Air Medals, who set a supersonic speed record from Los Angeles to New York in 1957, a devout Presbyterian from a small town in Ohio who married his childhood sweetheart, Annie, a family man who tape-recorded his daily diary and sent the tapes to his teen-age son and daughter at home in Virginia so they could hear his own voice and feel his absence less.

Americans, getting to know everything about John Glenn, subconsciously weighed the price of a man, a father, a pilot, against the cost of what he would achieve. Glenn himself worried about the public attention. Before the flight, in a White House chat with President Kennedy, he complained that the focus of interest on his person and personality was detracting from the scientific aspects of the flight that he considered much more important. But the President told him he could not separate the man from the mission. The success of one was the success of the other. For a people hungering for a hero, John Glenn's adventure would be their adventure.

Twice, Glenn had watched fellow astronauts roar off on missions for which he had also trained. Now he trained for his own flight, backed up by friend and fellow astronaut Scott Carpenter. He jogged along the beach to keep his weight down to a lean 168 pounds. He went through simulated countdowns and simulated flights to rehearse every detail he would eventually face. Experience, he said repeatedly, is the one bulwark against fear and failure.

"The more familiar you are with the shots," he said, "the less awesome they seem. But I don't think they'll ever stop being impressive, particularly if you think of yourself sitting there on top of the rocket waiting to be shot into space.

"Actually the second, third and fourth [orbital] flights may accomplish far more scientifically than the first flight does. The first mission is going to be a sort of 'Gee whiz, look at me, here I am, ma' type of deal. The second flight, once a man has been briefed on what to expect, should accomplish a lot more.

"Experience in dangerous and unexpected situations is even more valuable than good conditioning," Glenn said. "If you have successfully controlled your airplane in

Heroes Under Different Flags—Gherman Titov (left), the Soviet major who orbited the earth 17 times in 25 hours, passing even the most ambitious U.S. flight plans on schedule. But John Glenn's on-again, off-again first American orbit of the earth captured the world's imagination, and the freckled, red-headed Marine became the nation's greatest space hero.

an emergency, or dealt with an enemy whose prime object is to destroy you, your chances of making the proper decision the next time are increased."

Dates for the shot slipped by because of uncertainties here, problems there. Postponement followed postponement. By the end of January, almost 600 newsmen from the United States and 13 foreign countries were waiting at Cape Canaveral. The Voice of America was set to broadcast the flight in 36 languages, including English. It also would prepare a film of the flight to 107 countries in 41 languages.

Glenn came close on January 27. He awoke early, dressed in his silver spacesuit, took the transport van to the launch pad where banks of 48 searchlights played on the great ocean-spanning Atlas rocket and the Mercury spacecraft called Friendship 7. He had already endured four postponements, and this was the closest he had come yet. His green eyes bright with a smile, he waved and gave thumbs-up signs to friends along the way. His only acknowledgment of the danger had come the night before.

Glenn made a statement through a spokesman to the American people. He asked that they continue to support space exploration even if he should die on the morrow. "He wants you to understand," the spokesman said, "that he and we have reduced the risk as far as humanly possible, but that there is still risk. He recognizes the risk, that there could be a malfunction, that something could happen to him. He pointed out that pioneers have faced risks many times before, that Adm. Richard E. Byrd almost died in the Antarctic, but that didn't stop polar exploration."

Now Glenn rode up in the gantry elevator, entered the spacecraft and began the countdown checks. Dawn broke over the Atlantic, but it was dimmed by clouds covering the Cape. The countdown clock stopped and started and then waited. The clouds would not disappear. Finally, with 20 minutes to go to blastoff, space agency officials called their fifth postponement. Glenn finally emerged from the spacecraft, after five hours and 13 minutes inside, to wait for a better day. The television cameras clicked off, and some 75,000 people, many of whom had camped all night along the roads and beaches of the Cape, packed up and went home. John Glenn, long on the low residue diet required before a launch, walked into a local bakery and bought himself a loaf of onion pumpernickel bread to break the fast.

There were other postponements, but none so close. Glenn continued to say each time that there would be another day, that the added time would further insure the mission. Never through it all, and never through the space agency spokesmen, did anyone get the slightest notion of impatience, edginess or frustration from the spaceman. It didn't seem real.

The first man in space, Gagarin, said he sympathized with Glenn's plight and sent best wishes for a launch soon. "For me," he said, "there is nothing good in the postponement of Glenn's flight after a five-hour wait. There is a serious psychological and moral pressure exerted on him. To sit in a rocket for five hours and wait any minute for launching must be terrible and unpleasant." If so, Glenn gave no indication.

Twice the President of the United States expressed disappointment. He rode out each major delay on a direct telephone line to Mercury Control. When he was asked if it wouldn't be better to make one sweeping postponement until spring when the weather was better, the President said: "I know it is a strain to Col. Glenn and it has delayed our program, and it puts burdens on all of those who must make these decisions as to whether the mission should go or not. I think it has been very unfortunate. But I have taken the position that the judgment of those on the spot should be final in regards to this mission, and I will continue to take their judgment. I think that they would be reluctant to have it cancelled for another three or four months because it would slow our whole space program down at a time when we are making a concentrated effort in space."

February flicked by, a disappointing gray day at a time. Monster storms prowled the Atlantic where the spacecraft would splash down. Then, on the morning of the 20th, Glenn was awakened in the blue-walled quarters he shared with Carpenter. It

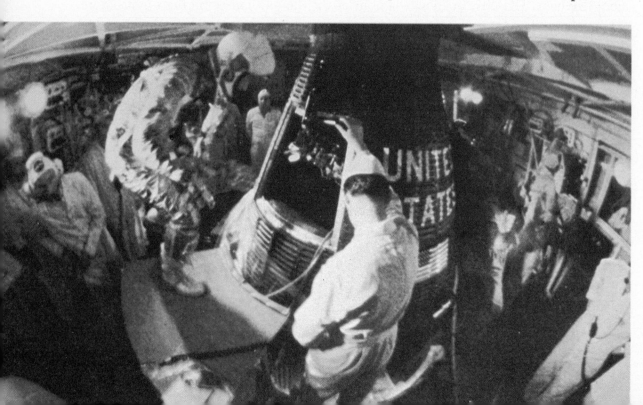

The Hatch Is Open—Friendship 7, atop an Atlas rocket, waits for its human pilot. Glenn, after nearly a dozen postponements, climbs aboard for his orbital flight.

was 2:20 a.m. Within 25 minutes he began the pre-flight ritual, clad in a white bath-robe, sitting down with friends to the steak breakfast, the final physical check, the stethoscope to the heart, the lungs, the probing light in the eyes, the ears, the throat. Then the fitting of the medical sensors to tattooed spots on his body so that doctors would know his physical condition by radio no matter what happened.

Finally, the silver suit again, one leg at a time, shrugging into the arms and shoulders, the zipping up, the dust-covers over his silver boots. The suit-check for leaks. The brisk walk out of Hangar S where he had lived those final days, smiling, waving with his right arm, and into the waiting transfer van. Ominously, above, the moon skittered behind light clouds, but the closer Glenn got to the launch pad, the heavier the clouds became.

Darkness still gripped the Cape, except for the 48 searchlights turned on the stark white rocket and its spacecraft, and the red gantry working tower, 16 stories high. Glenn stepped out of the transfer van and past the 200 technicians milling around the base of the rocket. He did not see the sign on a fence that said, "Complex 14 has worked 57 days without a serious accident."

Just before he entered the elevator the public address system announced the birth of a baby to one of the launch crew. "Well," said one veteran of the 10 postponements so far, "at least somebody got launched today."

By now the cloud cover was extensive over the entire Cape area. Thousands who had camped or slept in cars along the beaches were listening to radios and keeping an eye on the skies. At precisely 6 a.m., John Glenn rode the elevator up 12 stories to the spacecraft. In minutes he worked his way in, legs first, sliding into the couch molded months ago of glass fiber to fit his contour, to support him through the heavy gravity forces he would endure.

Small delays stalled the countdown. In Washington, President Kennedy, in his bedroom, began watching with most of the nation on television. Just before 8 a.m., the countdown resumed, and at almost the exact moment the sky brightened and the sun seemed to elbow its way through thinning cloud.

In the White House, the President went downstairs for a breakfast meeting with congressional leaders, watching the events on a portable television set with the sound turned down while they talked. They saw the gantry roll back, leaving the rocket, the spaceship, the man, standing alone, facing the sea and the sky after almost two-and-a-half months of waiting.

The space agency reported the weather was satisfactory at the Cape and in the Atlantic, and that the rocket and spacecraft were "Go." As the countdown moved on, the White House opened up a telephone to Mercury Control, and with three minutes to launch, the President took over the phone, standing and watching the television picture as the congressional leaders shifted chairs into position in a cluster around it.

In America, it was as if everything had stopped, all eyes, all ears keyed to this one sandy spit of land, this one man in a rocket. In Washington, the U.S. government came to a virtual halt. Typewriters stopped, television monopolized almost every office. In New York, foot traffic seemed to evaporate in Times Square as the city sought out television sets and radios. Bars with television did a bracing early morning business. In Grand Central Station some 5,000 commuters ignored their offices and stood in the mezzanine to watch the huge TV screen set up in the main concourse. Stores were nearly empty. Long distance and local telephone calls dropped off to nearly nil everywhere. In Atlanta, some 150 persons rushed in when a department store opened, but headed straight for the television display room. In New Concord, Ohio, John Glenn's hometown, some 800 people congregated in the college gymnasium to follow the launch.

Finally, at 9:47 a.m., the countdown swept past zero and the great yellow and orange flame kicked out of the Atlas rocket, billowing through the concrete launch pad, spending itself into dark gray smoke. And slowly, reluctantly, the 125-ton monster lifted itself from the earth to shove the 168-pound man toward space.

In Glenn's hometown, the crowd in the gymnasium was silent for one tortured moment and then it broke into cheers. In Grand Central Station, there were shrieks of "Go, go, go," and softer cries of "Make it John—God bless you," and women with tears in their eyes and men with audible prayers on their lips. In New York's subways, train loudspeakers crackled, "Attention, ladies and gentlemen. Col. John H. Glenn has just taken off in his rocket for orbit. Please say a little prayer for him."

"Go Straight, Go True, Go, Go, Go"—Glenn zooms into orbit, and on New York's subways the loudspeaker announced it and asked passengers to say a prayer for him.

In Mercury Control—Flight experts watched the path of Friendship 7 along the plotting boards. The blipping white light meant America was finally in orbit.

Glenn's first words were, "The clock is operating." He was in flight and the minutes of the flight clock were moving now. "It is a little bumpy along here," Glenn reported as the rocket built up speed. From the ground came the repeated assurance, "Flight path looks good." From Glenn came the mechanical readouts of the instruments, even when his voice became strained with the building acceleration. Seconds into the flight, Mercury Control called out, "Cape is go. We are standing by for you." "Roger," came the astronaut's voice. "Cape is go and I am go."

The booster engines cut off, the main rocket cut off, Glenn hurtled into orbit. "Zero Gs and I feel fine," he said. "Capsule is turning around. Oh, that view is tremendous! . . . I can see the booster doing turnabouts just a couple of hundred yards behind. It looks beautiful . . . Can see clear back, a big cloud pattern, away back toward the Cape. Beautiful sight! . . . The horizon is a brilliant blue. There I have the mainland in sight at present coming up through the scope [the periscope]. And have the Canaries [the Canary Islands off Africa] in sight through the window . . ."

Glenn was in orbit. America was in orbit. In Nebraska, an executive with Omaha's biggest department store was asked what the effect was on business. "I don't believe there has been any business," he answered. In Charlotte, N.C., a taxi company couldn't reach its drivers because they were all listening to newscasts on Glenn's progress.

From the Friendship 7, Glenn's voice was steady and business-like as he tried to record the immensity of the new view he had. "The only unusual thing I have noticed was the rather high, what appeared to be a haze layer up some seven or eight degrees above the horizon on the night side. The stars, I can see through it, as they go down toward the real horizon. But it is a very visible band, or layer . . . above the normal horizon . . . I had a lot of cloud cover coming off of Africa. It has thinned out considerably now, and although I cannot definitely see . . . there is a lot of moonlight here that reflects off of what clouds there are."

From fellow astronaut Gordon Cooper at an Australian tracking station, Glenn heard the reply, "Excellent, John. Shortly you may observe some lights down there. Do you want to take a check on that, to your right."

The people of the Australian city of Perth turned on their lights and stayed up late to become an earth beacon for Glenn's spacecraft high overhead. A businessman even offered to pay the bill for the extra hours of street lighting. The government declined.

Then Glenn saw it, the city of 450,000, lights on, shades up, laid out on the black earth below: "Just to my right I can see a big pattern of light, apparently right on the coast. I can see the outline of a town and a very bright light just to the south of it . . . The lights show up very well. Thank everybody for turning them on, will you?"

Glenn passed over Australia just before midnight. "That was sure a short day," he told Cooper on the ground below. "That was about the shortest day I have ever run into." He would be running in and out of days and nights for all his three orbits. "Time passes rapidly, eh?" Cooper asked. But it was Glenn who was passing rapidly through what earthlings call time.

His first problem came at the end of his first orbit when he told Mercury Control that the nose of his spacecraft tended to drift slightly to the right while it was on automatic pilot. It was due to a small control jet or thruster on the left side of the craft. To save on thruster fuel, Glenn reported, "I am on fly-by-wire now, I am controlling manually." "Roger," acknowledged Shepard at Mercury Control. "We concur here. Recommend you remain fly-by-wire." Now, Glenn would fly the spacecraft himself. If there had not been a man in the spacecraft to override the faulty automatic system, the spacecraft would have been brought down at the end of the first orbit.

Once, ignoring orders, Glenn opened the visor of his helmet, squinted his eyes to slits and looked at the naked sun. It was like a searing electric-arc, like one of the searchlights turned on his rocket a few hours ago. But he could look at it, unabbreviated by the earth's atmosphere, without tinted glass, without pain, for a moment.

Over the Pacific, a mystery. He thought for a few seconds he was looking into a new field of stars. But no. "There were thousands of little particles outside the cabin at sunrise over the Pacific. They were bright yellowish-green. About the size and intensity of a firefly on a real dark night. As far as I could look off to each side I could see them." He took a kidding about his fireflies later, until other spacemen saw them, too. "What did they say, John?" asked one psychiatrist. But flight experts had a pretty accurate notion of what they were from the start: water droplets from a cooling radiator on the spacecraft, frozen to crystal in the coldness of space, traveling with the ship that emitted them at a speed of nearly 17,500 miles an hour, glinting in the sun.

A new thing. Everything was new. The colors, unreproducible colors. Undescribable scenes. The sunrises. The sunsets. The earth below, the clouds in great white swirls. The human feeling in weightlessness. Hanging things in midair in front of you, on nothing, and finding them there when you looked again. The roll of camera film that flitted away from the fingers and was lost in the cabin.

Once more he was asked if he wanted to continue. The troubles with the thrusters now involved not only left to right action, but roll or spin action. "Affirmative," Glenn said quickly. "I'm ready to go." And on he went, to the third and last orbit of his trip, and his scariest time of all.

Now, some four hours after the voyage began, he was over the Pacific for the third time, heading for the United States, counting down for the firing of the braking rockets that would slow his speed and bring him to earth, a 23-minute descent he will never forget.

For almost an entire orbit, Mercury Control had worried over a warning light on the control panel. It indicated that the heat shield could be loose. If so, Glenn and the flight were both in peril. The heat shield, a glass fiber coating on the case of the bell-shaped spacecraft, was designed to burn away during the spacecraft's plunge into the earth's atmosphere. By burning, it would dissipate much of the 4,000-degree temperature built up by the friction between the spacecraft and the air. Without the heat shield the spacecraft and pilot would burn to dust in re-entry.

Gradually, as station after station around the earth checked with him on the heat shield's status, Glenn became aware that Mercury Control was worried. He wasn't told the trouble, and later complained he should have been. Meanwhile, flight experts huddled to deal with the problem. Was the heat shield really loose? Was the warning light in error? What could be done if the shield were loose? The answer seemed to be the retropack. This was a package of three small rockets strapped to the blunt end of the spacecraft below the heat shield. When they fired, they would brake the spacecraft's speed and bring it into a long looping landing on earth. Normally the straps would be broken and the rockets jettisoned after firing. But perhaps, reasoned Walt Williams, if the pack were kept on, the straps would hold the heat shield in place at least until the air pressure were sufficient to do the job. Glenn was told by Wally Schirra at the California tracking station to keep the retropack on.

All over America, those who had left their television sets and radios came back to them to hear the news of the latest hazard. In Washington, the House of Representatives halted debate on the debt limit for news of Glenn's flight. Democratic Leader Mike Mansfield told a virtually empty Senate that "in view of the circumstances" it

In Orbit—Glenn watched an empty applesauce tube float weightlessly away. He raised his visor once to squint at the sun—against orders—and he searched the blackness for stars.

would adjourn until the next day. But most of the senators already had adjourned to their offices and the cloakrooms to watch TV and listen to radios. Treasury Secretary Douglas Dillon and Commerce Secretary Luther Hodges watched on television in their offices. Defense Secretary Robert McNamara, just off a plane from Hawaii, listened on his limousine radio en route to the Pentagon. In his office he found Gen. Lyman Lemnitzer, chairman of the Joint Chiefs of Staff, watching on television.

At 2:20 p.m., the braking rockets fired aboard Friendship 7. The spacecraft began its descent. The stopping action of the rockets was so strong Glenn radioed, "I feel like I'm going back to Hawaii." Then he told Schirra, "It looks good, Wally. I'll see you back East." It was not all that sure at that moment.

Now Friendship 7 bucked into the earth's atmosphere. Glenn saw chunks of the retropack flash past his window in the fiery orange-red glow of the burning heat shield. He wasn't sure it was the retropack or the heat shield that was breaking up. His radio blacked out from the envelope of hot gases surrounding his ship. Glenn remembered years later his back could almost feel the heat that wasn't there. When the radio came on again, he reported with a bare tone of relief, "Boy, that was a real fireball!"

The spacecraft was wobbling wildly from side to side, beyond tolerable limits. Glenn, trying to control by hand, switched to autopilot. But then all of his control-system fuel tanks went dry. He reached out to release the stabilizing drogue parachute early in hopes it would settle the ship and avoid a nose-first landing. But before he could, the chute popped out automatically—then the main parachute. Not until then was he out of the woods. He splashed down in the Atlantic at 2:43 p.m., the heat shield sizzling when it hit the water. The recovery destroyer *Noa* was just six miles away, had him in sight, and was headed his way at flank speed. About 20 minutes later the spacecraft with its pilot still inside was set down on the ship's deck. Glenn

blew the hatch and emerged, five pounds lighter than he had weighed when he took off, most of it water loss in the hot spaceship. "My condition," reported the smiling astronaut, "is excellent."

His only wound was some skinned knuckles when he hit the trigger to blow the hatch open and it recoiled on his gloved hand. The flight had lasted four hours and 56 minutes, covered 81,000 miles of the earth's surface, sped from winter in the United States to summer in Australia, shuttled back and forth across the international dateline from February 20 to February 21, from Tuesday to Wednesday and back again.

Later, in the White House Rose Garden, President Kennedy told the nation, "I know that I express the great happiness and thanksgiving of all of us that Col. Glenn has completed his trip, and I know that this is particularly felt by Mrs. Glenn and his two children. I also want to say a word for all of those who participated with Col. Glenn at Canaveral. They faced many disappointments and delays—the burdens upon them were great. But they kept their heads and they made a judgment, and I think their judgment has been vindicated.

"We have a long way to go in this space race. We started late. But this is a new ocean, and I believe the United States must sail on it and be in a position second to none.

"Some months ago I said that I hoped every American would serve his country. Today Col. Glenn served his."

America seemed to reach out, in relief, pride and gratitude, to touch its new hero. He was compared with Columbus and with Charles Lindbergh, the Lone Eagle. In Freeport, N.Y., a baby boy born when Glenn re-entered the earth's atmosphere was named for him. Glenn was made a Kentucky Colonel while he was still in flight. In Larkspur, Calif., they named a park for him. In Auburn, Me., they named a street for him. In Maplewood, Minn., and in his hometown of New Concord they named high schools for him. In his home state of Ohio they named February 20 for him. He was made honorary citizen of a dozen towns, including Ottawa, Ill., and Quincy, Mass. New York City wanted him for a tickertape parade, and Liberal, Kan., wanted him to preside over its annual Pancake Day. At a New Jersey boat show they renamed the boats, "What Now, Nikita," "Orbit Four," and "Friendship 7." In New York, a congressman wanted to change the name of Cape Canaveral to Cape Glenn. Senators and representatives applauded him as proof of American superiority and as a "modern day Columbus." One wanted to vote him the Congressional Medal of Honor. Vice President Johnson said, "Outer space has now become a pathway for mankind and we hope and pray that it is a pathway to peace."

All over the United States, postmasters received a cryptic message from headquarters: "Open Package and Sell Stamps." The packages, sealed and stamped "Do Not Open," had been received days before. They contained special commemorative stamps for Glenn's flight, four-centers with a blue rectangle containing a spacecraft in the rays of the sun, soaring over the earth. They had been prepared in secret; the designer worked in Rome. The engraver in Washington labored only at night and on weekends. The stamps were printed in a locked press room. Now they were available. More than 70,000 were sold in the first two hours at the stamp collectors' window in Washington's Benjamin Franklin Post Office. Half a million stamps were sold in Baltimore in just two hours. But ironically, in Huntsville, Ala., which called itself since Explorer I "the space capital of the world," they didn't receive any stamps. Postmaster General Lowie Collier borrowed 25,000 stamps from the Birmingham Post Office and sold them until 9 that night.

Glenn kidded from space that his three orbits would qualify him for Marine Corps flight pay in the month of February. On his return to earth the Corps notified him that

Homeward Bound—Glenn chats with an engineer checking over the interior of Friendship 7, now safe aboard the destroyer *Noa* after three orbits of the earth. Glenn was heading home to tickertape parades, a hero's welcome from Congress, and a career that would dash from triumph to despair and back again.

his bonus would be $245. With 18 years of service, Glenn's monthly pay and allowances came to $1,149.68 including his flight pay. The space agency provided no extra pay.

Glenn was helicoptered from the *Noa* to the aircraft carrier *USS Randolph,* and from there to the debriefing station at Grand Turk Island in the Bahamas. Almost simultaneously, Donald (Deke) Slayton flew to Grand Turk to join Glenn and Carpenter, who was already there. Slayton was already slated to duplicate Glenn's flight in April. What the 37-year-old Slayton didn't know was that his frustration as an astronaut was to surpass all the others.

Glenn landed at Grand Turk just a few hours after sunset—the fourth sunset he had seen that day. He was greeted by backup pilot Carpenter who jabbed him playfully in the ribs. "It's been a long day," he told everybody. Then he turned himself over to the doctors and the experts who wanted to tape record every detail of his flight.

While Glenn was debriefed, his flight was going into the record books, behind two Soviet manned flights. The Russians had opened their files to the Federation Aeronautique Internationale and Gagarin's orbit was listed as the world's first.

First or last, Glenn's flight won cheers from Europe to the Far East. It was dinner time in Europe and bedtime in Japan when Glenn blasted off. But dinner, or bed, or not, Glenn was the center of attention. The Italian radio network broke into its regular programs to report Glenn's flight. In Austria, newspapers were flooded with questions. The British Broadcasting Corporation carried the Glenn flight in full, and broke into other programs to present a recorded interview with Glenn made weeks earlier. Even the Soviet news agency, *Tass,* carried the news—in a 71-word item.

Good wishes came from most world capitals. Only in some Communist countries was there less than enthusiasm. The East German radio and news agency called it "the great propaganda hullabaloo." Havana radio offered one sentence which noted only the launch, the 10 delays and Glenn's first orbit trouble. Moscow radio was broadcasting a condemnation of Cuban-U.S. relations while Glenn was coming back to earth. At the end of the Cuban item, the Russian announcer read a terse account of Glenn's flight, noting that it came 10 months after Gagarin's. Voice of America broadcasts to Russia were jammed.

But officially the Soviets were cordial. The day after the flight, Premier Khrushchev and the Soviet cosmonauts praised the Glenn flight. Khrushchev suggested the two nations pool their space efforts, echoing an earlier Kennedy proposal, and the Soviet leader added that the earth does not seem so large anymore. President Kennedy was quick to respond. He said he hoped Soviet and U.S. representatives could meet at an early date to discuss means to cooperate in space. "When men reach beyond this planet," Kennedy said, "they should leave their national differences behind them. All men will benefit, if we can invoke the wonders of science instead of its terrors."

Yet this exchange would do little to cool the space race, the score of which was rapidly changing. To date, the United States had launched 69 satellites to 13 for the Soviet Union. Thirty-five of the U.S. satellites were still flying to one for the Soviet Union. Now the United States had orbited a man, and there was more to come.

# 5 The New Ocean

On February 23, 1962, a Friday, three days after his flight, John Glenn came full circle to the place it all began, Cape Canaveral. There he saw again his wife and his children, and there he met again the President who set the nation on a course for the moon. But, most of all, there his hero's welcome began, the largest for any pioneer since Lindbergh.

Still in seclusion on Grand Turk Island, Glenn was reported "a wee bit nervous," as his return home approached. Ahead of him was an appearance before a joint session of Congress, a tickertape parade in New York City, a star-spangled welcome by his hometown. If the Broadway parade was the big show, then the motorcade to Cape Canaveral through the town of Cocoa Beach was the out-of-town tryout.

A red-white-and-blue banner stretched across Florida State Highway A1A, the main street of Cocoa Beach. It proclaimed, "Welcome Back, John." His family and parents waited at Patrick Air Force Base, escorted to Florida by President Kennedy, who spent a few days at the home of his ailing father in West Palm Beach. Vice President Johnson flew to Grand Turk to bring Glenn back. On the plane bound for Florida, Johnson told the astronaut, "In my country, we'd say you're pretty tall cotton." Glenn laughed.

They talked about Glenn's address to Congress. Johnson suggested he keep it short and simple. "There will be no Republican-Democratic dividing line in Congress when you make your little talk," he said. "They are all together on this." Johnson thought a bit and added, "Usually this honor is reserved only for heads of state and presidents, but in this case, the whole country elected you."

They landed at Patrick Air Force Base. Escorted by the Secret Service, Glenn and the Vice President stepped off the plane to the applause of the crowd. An Air Force honor guard snapped to attention and present arms. Glenn embraced his daughter, then hugged and kissed his wife, Annie. There were tears in his eyes.

Before they left the base for the 20-mile trip to Cape Canaveral's launching pads, the Vice President stepped to a microphone and said, "It's a great pleasure to welcome home a great pioneer of history." He pointed out that Glenn's flight had brought a proposal from Khrushchev that the United States and the Soviet Union pool their space resources. "So, colonel," he said, "you must feel you have done something that two presidents have been unable to do . . . It's good to have you back, John."

Glenn made a few remarks, retaining the editorial "we" that he said stood for the entire space team. The motorcade with each of the seven astronauts in a separate car headed north for the Cape. Some 100,000 people lined the way, including almost all the 6,124 residents of Cocoa Beach. One motel had a sign all week that said, "The hopes and prayers of the whole world are with you, Col. Glenn." Now the sign said, "Our prayers have been answered."

All along the way, high school bands struck up with the Marine Corps hymn, and one woman hoisted her baby over her head above the crowd. "See," she said, "he's the one waving. You remember this. You remember you saw him." Twice the hero's white convertible stopped, the first time when the Vice President spotted a 2-year-old boy wearing a toy space helmet, sitting on his father's shoulders. He motioned them over to the car and introduced the boy to Glenn. At each stop, the crowd encircled the car, and each time it took 10 minutes to get under way again. Along the way, Glenn gave his wife a small gold and ruby pin he had carried into space for her. "I'm so proud of it," she kept exclaiming. "Isn't it beautiful?"

Then at the gate of the launch center on the Cape, Glenn performed the most useless gesture of the day. He showed his identification card to the guard. No one looked at the card. Everyone looked at Glenn.

When the President's plane landed at the Cape airstrip, the Glenn party was waiting. It was Kennedy's first trip to the Cape that would one day bear his name. President Eisenhower had visited there before when the space base was still an infant. Together, the President and Glenn toured the Cape. They stopped at Launch Pad 14 where Glenn began his flight exactly three days, one hour and 36 minutes earlier. The President stepped to the microphone and grinned, "He wants to come back and thank you—I think."

Then they went to Hangar S where Glenn had waited out those dreary postponements. There stood Glenn's Friendship 7 spaceship, fished from the sea and awaiting study before it was sent to the Smithsonian Institution in Washington. The President gave Glenn and Project Mercury director Robert Gilruth the space agency's Distinguished Service Medal.

"Seventeen years ago the Marines planted the American flag on Mt. Suribachi [on Iwo Jima]," the President said. "And . . . maybe in the not too distant future, Col. Glenn and the Marine Corps, or a Navy man, or an airman will plant the American flag on the moon.

"Our boosters may not be as large as some others," the President added, "but our men and women are."

In the days that followed, Glenn went into seclusion with his family before his appearance before Congress, an extraordinary session with some legislators holding small children on their laps. After the Supreme Court filed into the House Chamber,

William M. (Fishbait) Miller, the doorkeeper, stood at the head of the center aisle and called out, "Mr. Speaker, Lt. Col. John H. Glenn Jr. of the United States Marine Corps."

With that, the hall full of lawmakers and dignitaries including the Joint Chiefs of Staff rose and turned, applauding loudly and smiling, as Glenn in a gray suit strode down the aisle to the podium. "Today I know that I seem to be standing alone on this great platform," he said, "just as I seemed to be alone in the cockpit of the Friendship 7 spacecraft. But I am not.

"There were with me then—and with me now—thousands of Americans and many hundreds of citizens of many countries around the world who contributed to the truly international undertaking voluntarily in a spirit of cooperation and understanding . . . As our knowledge of the universe in which we live increases, may God grant us the wisdom and guidance to use it wisely."

Glenn was cheered by a quarter of a million persons in the rain in Washington. He was hailed by four million in the winter sun in New York City. He was received by cheers in a dozen languages at the United Nations. And he was the focus of 50,000 persons who jammed the 2,000-population town where he grew up.

America had its hero. Now the hard work began. The danger and the adventure were just beginning. But for most Americans there would not be another moment like this for years to come.

In 1960 the space agency had only 10,000 employes. In 1962 it had 22,000. Besides these staff personnel, it had the aid of aerospace firms on contract. These firms had 36,000 employes working on space agency contracts in 1960. By 1962 that number had grown to 115,000, and was still going up.

Behind it all was money. The flights of Shepard, Grissom and Glenn had put meat on the President's space race challenge to go to the moon. The three astronauts testified on behalf of the space agency's budget request for fiscal 1963. The space agency

"Seventeen Years Ago . . . Mt. Suribachi"—And "maybe in the not too distant future," said President Kennedy, "Col. Glenn and the Marine Corps, or a Navy man, or an airman will plant the American flag on the moon." But for now, Vice President Johnson, the President and Glenn inspect Friendship 7, as some other men had looked and wondered at the mechanical creature of Kitty Hawk.

wanted almost $3.8 billion. Congress chopped off a little more than $140 million. Coupled with Defense Department space spending, it meant $5 billion a year for the space effort.

All of that from nothing four years before. In fiscal 1959, the space agency spent less than $11 million on manned space flight. By 1960 that figure had multiplied 10 times. In fiscal 1961 the space agency spent $279 million on manned space flight, and doubled that figure for 1962. For unmanned satellites and space exploration, the agency spent less than $25 million in 1959, multiplied that amount five times for 1960. By 1962, it was spending $360 million for unmanned space exploration.

It was becoming a sophisticated and expensive operation, as forecast. Now Apollo and its mammoth Saturn rocket were coming off the drawing boards. The hardware for the two-man Gemini spaceship was being hammered out to perfect the techniques of rendezvous in space and to prove ultimately that a man could work in space wearing only a protective spacesuit. At the same time the space agency was getting ready to shift its manned flight operations to Houston, Tex., where it would build a $312-million plant from scratch on donated land.

And while all of this was going on the space agency witnessed its first personal tragedy. On the eve of his first flight into space, it saw one of the seven astronauts, Donald Kent Slayton, dropped from the flight qualified list because of a flutter in his heart. The announcement was made on March 15, 1962. He had been scheduled to duplicate Glenn's mission in April. Now he was replaced by Scott Carpenter, who had practiced almost 80 hours for the mission as Glenn's understudy. Slayton's heartbeat had been a question mark since the summer of 1959 when doctors noted a small irregularity in the beat during tests in a high speed centrifuge. From then on Slayton had been checked out by top flight surgeons and civilian specialists. Most could not see a problem that would bar him from flight. But a final panel of civilian cardiologists reported that they would not guarantee that Slayton's heart irregularity could not impair him during flight. That being the case, they said, it would be wise to choose an astronaut without the heart problem if one were available.

Carpenter, 37, a small scar over his left eye from hitting a radiator when he climbed from the crib at the age of 1, was a different kind of astronaut. His parents were divorced. He was a self-admitted drifter and "a sort of a no-good," as a youth. He once jumped from a school window to avoid being kept after class. He quit high school football because he couldn't devote himself to learning the plays. He didn't study hard and he admitted to stealing things from stores. Twice he flunked out of college, becoming a day laborer in Colorado, his home state. It wasn't until he had a serious auto accident that left him unconscious for four days that he decided to change his way of life. He returned to college, then rejoined the Navy and became a test pilot. He also became careful and reflective. Said one Project Mercury psychiatrist: "One man, given 10 seconds to make a decision, would make it in the first second. Carpenter, given the same time, would think over the alternatives, then decide at the last second."

On May 24, 1962, he flashed into orbit, his pretty, blonde wife Rene watching from the beach. She was the first Mercury wife to view her husband's launch firsthand. "We often feel emotionally drained, and we tend to fall back on such words as happy, proud, or thrilled," she said, "and we feel so much more."

Carpenter's Aurora 7 spaceship released a small multicolored balloon in space for two experiments. Carpenter was to report which colors showed up best—a daylight orange and silver-aluminum. And he was to determine whether the balloon encountered any air resistance at the orbital altitude. It did not. In fact the balloon failed to show any pattern to its movements. Sometimes the line connecting it to the spacecraft remained in coils as it had been packed.

With film for more than 600 pictures, Carpenter concentrated on a variety of shots with special film. He photographed the image of the sun flattened by the earth's horizon at sunset, recorded a star slipping into the haze layer above the earth's horizon, and filmed cloud cover for the U.S. Weather Bureau. Accidentally, he thumped the side of the spacecraft and produced a cloud of the "fireflies" that Glenn had seen. Carpenter saw them earlier too, describing them as snowflakes. He found he could produce them at will, simply by hitting the side of the spacecraft and knocking off the frost crystals. He also discovered he could alter the position of the spacecraft by moving his arms and shifting his weight inside.

The press of all his experimenting was to cause him trouble in the moments to come. His flight was almost terminated at the end of the second orbit because he was running short of fuel for his attitude control system. Now nearing the end of his flight, he was behind in his checklists. When he finally fired his retrorockets to brake the spacecraft's speed, he fired them late and was not holding the spacecraft at the right position. On the ground, Mercury Control could see he was going to land well past the target area. Carpenter had compounded his fuel supply problem by leaving two control systems on at the same time, unnoticed because he was busy with other things. Fuel was tight as the spacecraft hurtled earthward, and control of its position was essential. Flying Aurora 7 in a semi-manual method, Carpenter was buffeted by severe oscillations on his descent. He splashed down 250 miles beyond the target point, out of sight and out of radio range. For about 35 minutes he was virtually lost to Mercury Control and Americans following the flight on television. Actually during this time, recovery aircraft had a fix on his homing radio beacon aboard the spacecraft, but no one knew it.

Hot and hungry, Carpenter struggled out of the narrow neck of the spacecraft, inflated a life raft and got in, still clutching the camera and the pictures he had taken in space. When planes came in view, they found the astronaut reclining in the raft eating the bite-size candy and snacks from the survival kit's food supply.

On Grand Turk Island for debriefing, Carpenter was received by John Glenn. The two embraced and Glenn rubbed Carpenter's cheek with his own, and wiped a tear from his eye. The next day Carpenter stepped to the back porch of the small hospital where he was being checked and made a statement to newsmen. "I should apologize now," he said, "that it was a real cliffhanger. It kept a lot of people, including my

Enter Schirra—On his way to a textbook flight, Wally Schirra is helped into his Sigma 7 spaceship by back-up pilot Gordon Cooper and friends.

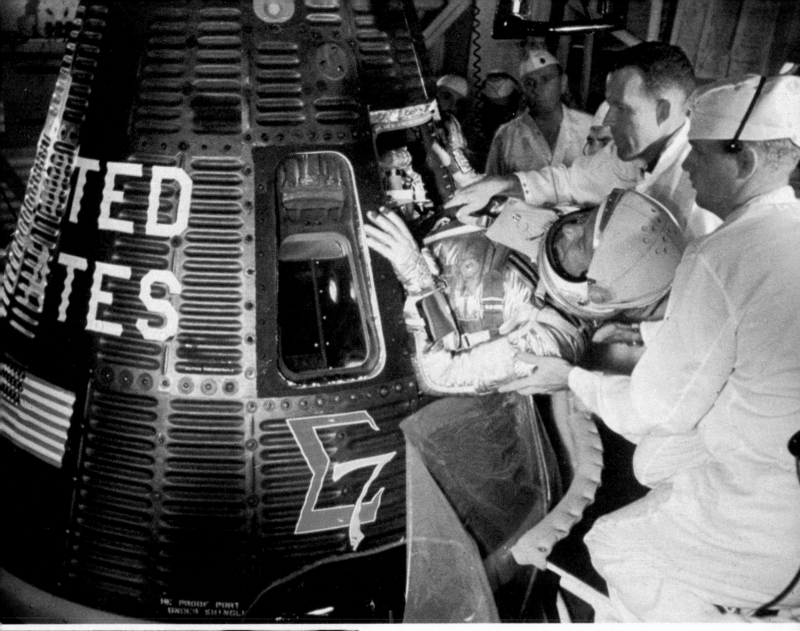

Exit Carpenter—After a cliffhanger, the viewer of sunsets in space, where they are all the same, is happy to be home, where they are all different.

family and people in the control center, worried. No one knew where I was, and I didn't either."

Carpenter's flight, like Glenn's before him, provided more information on how to streamline the Mercury spacecraft, stripping away unnecessary and heavy equipment for flights that would take longer and require more fuel. Three-orbit missions were all that had been planned for originally in Mercury. Now it would reach beyond. The space agency announced in mid-1962 that Wally Schirra would fly a six-orbit Mercury mission, perhaps in September.

After the Carpenter return, he and flight director Walt Williams visited President Kennedy at the White House. The President, relaxed, chatted with them as they waited for the car to come up the White House drive. Space flight, Kennedy said, was terribly important. "God knows," he said, "it's expensive. But I still think it's very worthwhile.

"We have three ways of combatting the Soviets. One is all-out nuclear war, which we don't want to do. Then, economically, and we're doing that. That's a long term process. Then we have to compete with them for the imagination of the rest of the world. This is one thing you can do for us. This really is competition."

If it looked as if the United States was going to win in mid-1962, the picture completely changed in August. The Soviet Union, on August 11, hurled Maj. Andrian G. Nikolayev and his Vostok III spaceship into orbit, following it the next day with Lt. Col. Pavel Popovich in Vostok IV, and a nearly identical orbit. Through the next days the spacecraft were tracked between three and 300 miles of each other, but apparently

Climb The Highest Mountain —Gordon Cooper's visit above the high Himalayas. Can you see the pattern of villages and chimneys from space?

did not rendezvous. It still was a tour de force the United States could not even approach. While Nikolayev, called Falcon, and Popovich, called Golden Eagle, talked back and forth between spaceships that weighed twice as much as the U.S. Mercury craft, the United States didn't even appear to be in the space race.

On August 15, the two Soviet spaceships landed within six minutes of each other. Nikolayev had turned 64 orbits in 94 hours and 35 minutes. Popovich had spun around the earth 48 times in 70 hours. It all made Schirra's coming six-orbit try look small indeed.

On October 3, 1962, Wally Schirra became the fifth American into space, the third into orbit. Right off the bat there was some minor trouble. The Atlas rocket was consuming fuel at too rapid a rate. The range safety officer came close to aborting the mission by blowing up the Atlas. But in seconds the problem moderated, and he decided to let the mission continue. "At a time like that," he said later, "a range safety officer doesn't have a friend in the world. There were only a very few seconds in which to analyze the situation and make a decision . . . We couldn't prove conclusively that we weren't going to make it.

"If the Atlas burned even one-fourth of a second less than the prescribed five minutes and five seconds," he said, "the capsule would not achieve orbit and would land in the Pacific Ocean or someplace else short of a complete orbit."

Nevertheless the launch was the most perfect to date, and Schirra's six orbits matched it. There was one more hairy moment on the ground. At the end of the first orbit, with his suit temperature running high, flight controllers came within 90 seconds of terminating the flight. But the suit temperature too began to drop, and they allowed the flight to continue.

Schirra's flight was designed for endurance. He carried the same amount of fuel to control spacecraft position as did Glenn and Carpenter, both of whom almost ran out in the waning minutes of flight. By allowing his spacecraft to drift, Schirra's job was to conserve as much fuel as possible to pave the way for longer missions in the Mercury spacecraft. As he lazed his way through space he saw powerful flares on the ground in Australia, and again the lights of the city of Perth, and he was seen himself by men aboard a tracking ship in the Indian Ocean. His Sigma 7 spacecraft, over 100 miles high, looked like a star, almost as bright as the planet Venus.

Talking with Glenn at a California tracking station, Schirra's cheerful voice summed it up, "I am real happy with this bird . . . All systems are green. I've got the suit temperature under control, as you know by now. And a delightful report for one John Glenn. I, too, see fireflies . . ."

The perfect flight had a perfect ending. Schirra splashed down less than four miles off the landing zone and just 9,000 yards ahead of the recovery carrier, the USS *Kearsarge* in the Pacific near Midway Island. It was the first Pacific landing for a U.S. spaceship. The nine-hour, 13-minute mission was called a textbook flight, and Schirra said he was "healthy as a bear . . . happy as a lark . . . I feel fine . . . What a sweet little bird."

Yet oddly there was a problem. Flight surgeons got a new realization of what weightlessness can do to the human body. Schirra showed signs of a physical condition called orthostatic hypotension. In effect, his heart had grown lazy. Pumping blood through his body in a weightless state was much easier than pumping blood in a one-gravity or earth gravity state. The heart, given a nine-hour vacation, became used to the lower work load. When Schirra stepped from his spacecraft he discovered his heart wasn't quite up to contending with gravity so quickly. His blood tended to pool in his legs. His blood pressure was down. His heart was beating fast to make up for its weakness. But the condition didn't last long. The heart gains strength back quickly, too. However, flight surgeons had a new problem to deal with, one that could probably be solved with exercise, but another reminder nevertheless that man was facing new stresses in his new adventure into space.

There was no big Washington reception, no tickertape parade through Manhattan. If the nation was preoccupied with other things, it would be brought up short quickly by a new development in the cold war. Even when he hosted the Schirras at a quiet gathering in his office 13 days after the flight, President Kennedy was embroiled in the new international developments but trying to keep it a secret while the National Security Council debated what to do about a new Soviet threat. The Schirra family visited the President in mid-October and the President took immediately to Susie Schirra, 5, and the youngest of the two Schirra children. He asked her if she had seen the White House ponies kept for his children. She said she hadn't. He took her for a ride on Caroline's pony, Macaroni, and offered her candy in his office. She took one bite and spit it out. The President laughed, confided he didn't eat it either, and asked her to tell him what kind she liked and he'd have it available the next time. There was no sign of his preoccupation. But he re-entered Security Council meetings later that day. In less than a week, he announced to the American public that Soviet missiles were being erected in Cuba that could bring half the nation within their range. He also announced a naval quarantine of Cuba until the missiles were removed. Until then the Schirras did not know that a shadow hung over the White House the day of their visit.

Nine special Americans also watched Schirra's flight with interest, eight of them witnessing it firsthand at Cape Canaveral. They were the new group of astronauts, pilots all, but with an accent on engineering and design. One of them, James A. Lovell Jr., explained that their prime interest was in the coming programs of Gemini and Apollo. "We hope they will go as smoothly as Schirra's flight," he said. His fellow fledglings were Neil Armstrong, Frank Borman, Charles Conrad Jr., James A. McDivitt, Thomas P. Stafford, Edward H. White II, John W. Young and Elliott M. See Jr.

In the coming years they would perfect new spacecraft and the techniques of space hunt and rendezvous. They would pioneer America's walks in space. And they would give the world startling close-up pictures of the black and white moon with the many-colored planet called earth off the horizon. Yet, for all the glory they would gather, two of them would not live to see the first American land on the moon.

Back From Space—Cooper gets help from ordinary sailors and a rowboat.

No one could guess this then. No one would have tried. Flight officials were looking for a measure of how far they could push the Mercury spacecraft. A quiet test pilot from Oklahoma showed them how far. Gordon Cooper, the last of the original seven astronauts qualified to fly, drew the assignment. He would ride the Mercury spaceship around the earth 22 times in May 1963.

At 36, Cooper was the youngest of the first seven. His father was an Air Force colonel, and a friend of pioneer aviators like Wiley Post and Amelia Earhart. Cooper first touched the controls of an airplane at 6, and soloed at 16. As a child, he remembered reading Buck Rogers in the Sunday comics and wondering whether man would fly into space before the 25th century. As an astronaut he had waited patiently for an assignment. Before one of the early flights he was asked to run through the pre-flight role of an astronaut in a demonstration for newsmen. He donned the silver space suit and went through the entire morning-of-flight sequence until he arrived at the launch pad. He walked slowly to the elevator that would take the real astronaut up to the Mercury spacecraft atop the rocket. But there he stopped. Hands clutching the door jamb as if he were being shoved inside against his will, Gordo, as his friends called him, mimicked panic and shouted, "No. No. I won't go! You can't make me!" And all the while the cameras clicked and the movies ground on, exposing film that would never be used.

Gordo's first date with space, May 14, was delayed because space officials couldn't get a diesel engine going to move back the working tower. Then it was postponed because a tracking radar went out of order. But on May 15, two years and 10 days since Shepard's pioneering flight, Cooper roared into orbit just four minutes late, the most perfect countdown so far. He named his spacecraft Faith 7.

From the beginning, the casual, relaxed astronaut was a study in contrast. He was off on the biggest adventure most men could imagine, but he might as well have been dozing off to sleep on a park bench in the sun. When business applied, he rattled off the required readings. Otherwise, he might have been in hibernation. "Great sport, isn't it?" beamed Schirra from the ground. "Sure is," replied the laconic Cooper. After two hours his oxygen consumption was so low, the ground controller laughingly advised him he could start breathing now.

In the early orbit, a small television camera in the spacecraft beamed down to earth the first pictures of an American astronaut while in orbit. "You look pretty casual," Shepard said from Mercury Control. "I am," grunted Cooper from orbit. By the time he had finished his second orbit, he confessed to the ground that he had fallen asleep briefly. It set the pattern for the flight. Doctors watched the radioed reports of his breathing and heart rate, picked up the sleep pattern. Thereafter they didn't bother him when they noticed he had dropped off to sleep.

But for all of this low-key behavior, Cooper played an ace observer in the skies. His final report was the most vivid any astronaut had given so far on the wonders of space. "I never tired of looking at the sunsets," he said. "As the sun begins to get down toward the horizon, it is very well defined . . . It is a very bright white; almost the bluish-white color of an arc lamp. As it begins to impinge on the horizon, it undergoes a spreading, or flattening, effect. The sky begins to get quite dark . . . This light spreading out from the sun is a bright orange color which moves out under a narrow band of bright blue that is always visible throughout the daylight period. As the sun sets farther, it is replaced by a bright gold-orange band which extends out for some distance on either side, defining the horizon even more clearly. The sun goes below the horizon rapidly, and the orange band still persists but gets considerably fainter as the black sky bounded by dark blue bands follow it down.

"When there is no moon," he said, "the earth is darker than the sky; there is a difference in the two blacks. In general there is more light from the sky; the sky is a shining black as compared with a dull black appearance of earth."

While he was short in his communications with earth, he fed his observations into his tape recorder, and he told of seeing myriad things from more than 100 miles up. He claimed to have seen a truck, a boat and a train.

But space officials later explained that he saw these things in context with the land features around them. From a cloud of dust moving along the skinny outline of a road, he deduced a truck. From the moving tip of an arrow-like wake in the water, he deduced a boat. From a moving point trailing smoke along a countryside, he deduced a train. He saw village-like patterns high in the Himalayas, and from these patterns trails of smoke. He deduced chimneys.

It wasn't until the 19th orbit that Cooper had any hint of trouble. But when it came, it gathered quickly into one of the most dramatic and frightening moments in the space program. A green light came on in the spacecraft indicating that the ship was heading back to earth. Cooper kept hoping it would just go away. It didn't. Ultimately, he turned it off so he wouldn't have to look at it. But it worried him and the experts in Mercury Control.

It was quite obviously a faulty reading. But what caused it? And what did it mean to the safety of the mission? The flight experts, geared up for such an emergency, began checking duplicate equipment at the plant where the spacecraft was made in St. Louis, and at the Cape. Hurry-up conferences produced a probable answer. The trouble apparently was in the electrical system, a surge of electrical power triggering the light.

But while all of this was going on, the problem in the spacecraft was becoming more serious. On the next orbit Cooper lost the instruments that told him just what position the spacecraft was in. Recurrent surges of electricity deviled the system. On the following orbit, the 21st, there was a major short circuit, cutting off all electrical power to the automatic control system, the autopilot. Now there was real trouble. Cooper would have to keep absolute control over the spacecraft with manual and semimanual systems, firing his braking rockets by hand as Carpenter had done, and flying the spacecraft through the wild buffeting and the furnace of re-entry. This time if the pilot failed, he was lost. Doctors ordered Cooper to take a pep pill to insure his alertness in the critical time ahead.

John Glenn, manning the tracking ship *Coastal Sentry* south of Japan, quickly worked out a manual sequence to broadcast back to Cooper in space. "We have a lot of stuff for you to copy, Gordo," he beamed up. "This retrorocket procedure. Are you ready for a clock command?"

The spacecraft's clock was reset so Cooper could use it to measure the split seconds when he would have to push the buttons firing the braking rockets. Glenn quickly listed the new procedure, Cooper copying it in the spacecraft. "No. 1 is attitude permission bypass," Glenn said. "Attitude permission bypass is No. 1. Do you acknowledge? Over." His voice without a trace of worry clicked the items off, and the two pilots, one in space and the other on the earth, set the events whereby man would overcome the failure of machine. "Retrorocket armed switch manual . . . Fly-by-wire stress collect switch, high and low . . . Retrorocket sequence switch No. 2 . . .

On The *USS Kearsarge*—Cooper, talked down from the skies by men on the ground like an old aviator lost in bad weather, peeks out from his spaceship, Faith 7, after being aloft just 51 minutes more than Lindbergh—traveling 600,000 miles.

That puts you on manual. If you'd want to go fly-by-wire, all you'd have to do is pull the manual handle off and your mode select to fly-by-wire. Roger?"

Cooper's voice steady, he acknowledged each item. To Americans eavesdropping on the conversation it was the movie theme, the pilot in the stricken aircraft being talked down by the tower on the ground. The image was not far from fact. Glenn counted down for Cooper to the precise second of firing the braking rockets.

Glenn: "Okay, your next 10-second count will be a countdown to your manual retro. Over."

Cooper: "Roger. I got that."

Glenn: "10-9-8-7-6-5-4-3-2-1, retrofire. Roger. A green here. Roger. How's your attitude, old Gordo?"

Cooper: "Real great."

Glenn: "Good show, boy. Real fine. Looked like you came off right on the money on time."

Cooper: "Roger. I think so."

Glenn: "Roger. Real good. On your next mark, 60 seconds from that retro, you should jettison retro. And you'll do that one manually. Right?"

Cooper: "Roger."

Glenn: "Got any estimate on your attitude hold? And any axis on how far you drifted off on retro? Over."

Cooper: "No, I sure don't. [garble] I couldn't guess. [lost in static]"

Glenn: "Good hit. [both laugh heartily]"

Cooper: "And off goes Johnny. [the retrorockets jettison]"

Glenn: "Roger. We have your signal. Okay, dealer's choice on re-entry. Fly-by-wire or manual . . ."

There were a few last minute instructions for the tortured time ahead as Cooper's spacecraft began the long looping trajectory that would bring it to earth. "It's been a real fine flight, Gordo," Glenn said. "Beautiful all the way. Everything."

The concerned voices of Mercury Control broke in with a question to the spacecraft, but Glenn shortstopped it. "Cape? CSQ," he said. "He looks real good. He held it very close, very tight. They were right on time on our marks here, and it came out. They looked good, sounded good and were good." When Cooper came out of the blackout of re-entry, Scott Carpenter picked up the splashdown events, checking them with the pilot.

The tension wasn't over until Cooper's Faith 7 spacecraft hove into view, just four miles in front of the prime recovery ship, the *Kearsarge*. Despite the trouble, he landed right on the money, safe and fairly sound. Doctors discovered the same problem that had existed with Schirra post-flight. The lazy heart from weightless flight was more severe in Cooper because he had been in a weightless state longer, but still only a slight case. The 147-pound pilot was dehydrated, had lost seven pounds, mostly in water, since he suited up the day before.

The dramatic elements of the flight awoke Americans again to the fact that this was still a pioneering, primitive program, not quite like the takeoffs and landings at the local airport.

Cooper's flight, covering 600,000 miles, took 34 hours, 20 minutes and 30 seconds. It was just 51 minutes more than it took Charles Lindbergh to fly the Spirit of St. Louis 3,610 miles across the Atlantic just 36 years before.

President Kennedy, trying to stick to his office routine, kept wandering into his secretary's office during the flight to watch for a moment on her television set, which was always on. Now, with the flight over, he made the traditional telephone call to Cooper aboard the carrier. "That was a great flight," the President told him. Later, in a telecast to the nation, Kennedy said, "Peace has her victories as well as war, and this was one of the victories for the human spirit today."

A quarter of a million turned out in Washington to hail the returning hero in town for a visit with the President and a short speech to a joint session of Congress. Cooper read the lawmakers a prayer he had composed aboard Faith 7, inspired by the wonder of space. It said in part, "Thank You . . . To be in this wondrous place, seeing all these startling, wonderful things You have created. Help guide and direct all of us that we may shape our lives to be much better Christians. So that we help one another and work with one another rather than fighting and bickering."

Next there was a tickertape parade in Manhattan. The city Sanitation Department, which measures and rues such events, reported that 2,900 tons of shredded paper flew down on city streets for Cooper. In the record books there were these earlier compilations: 3,474 tons for John Glenn; 3,249 tons for Gen. Douglas MacArthur, and 1,750 tons for Lindbergh.

Topping off his day in New York, Cooper took his wife, Trudy, to a Broadway show. It was a musical entitled "Stop The World, I Want To Get Off."

When the celebrating was over, Project Mercury officials pondered the future for a program that had already gone far beyond its original targets. There was considerable feeling that Mercury should go on, perhaps to a 72-hour flight. The two-man Gemini spaceships were still almost two years away. The idea of going two years without a manned flight would just be an invitation to the Soviets to increase their lead.

Those arguments could not change the facts. The objective was the moon. The way to attain that objective was to concentrate on the coming programs, not on merely compiling more hours in space. In mid-1963, a month after Cooper's flight, space agency officials closed the book on Project Mercury.

# 6 Two Years In Waiting

Behind the glamour and the heroes, there was another kind of man. He was one of the anonymous thousands who worked late through the night and into the morning tinkering with valves, checking electrical fittings, cleaning lines. He was a new kind of mechanic, sweating over a vehicle without wheels or wings, a vehicle so delicate yet so powerful that his smallest error could turn it into a raging orange fireball of failure.

One of these men, no one remembers his name now, worked late into the winter night in 1962, preparing an Atlas rocket to hurl a probe at the moon. The time when the moon would be in target position was flying by. He slaved for hours cleaning the fuel tank, repairing a leaky seal. Now he emerged, exhausted, coughing and spitting, fouling the clear night air with the stench of kerosene and sweat. He straightened up and stood there, framed by the glare of the searchlights with the gleaming white rocket towering above him. And he looked into the black velvet sky at the silver sphere in its zenith, and his face was frustrated and angry, and he shook his fist at the sky, and hurled obscenities at the moon.

To those who saw him and those who heard about him, that futile image captured more of the meaning of Cape Canaveral than all of the heroes in silver spacesuits, all of the dash and glitter of success.

With Cooper's flight over and Project Mercury ended, progress fell solely into the hands of the mechanics and engineers, the flight experts and designers, the men who worked with the tedious intricacies of the space age. It would be nearly two years before another American would fly into space, two years of working and waiting. But they would be eventful years. A president would die of an assassin's bullet. The space program he gave life and meaning would grow into maturity.

Of seven original astronauts, only three would still be qualified to fly. There would be new astronauts, expert in more than flying. There would be a new, expensive space center rising in Texas to rival Cape Canaveral. And even the name Cape Canaveral would change. By the time two years passed, the United States would be ready to launch men into space at two-month intervals and less. The nation that started second would take every world space record on the books. And all of that began with these years of toil and accident on earth.

Cape Canaveral spawned two worlds. First there was the fenced-in wilderness where the gantry towers rose from the sand and palmetto along the brink of the Atlantic. Here were the hangars and the fuel tank farms and the lumbering trucks laden with liquid oxygen and liquid nitrogen, and the control centers, and the people who worked three shifts a day. And all around this space complex was the cluster of would-be towns, awakening with new people. The biggest boomtown of the bunch was Cocoa Beach.

In the days of Vanguard and Explorer, in 1957 and 1958, it was a sometimes resort town with one motel, a few restaurants, serving the Miami-bound tourist. Its beaches at low tide were as wide as a football field, and clean. But the season was short. Seafront property could be bought for a few hundred dollars a lot. The overwhelming fact of its economic life was Patrick Air Force Base on its southern fringe. Straddling an oceanside state highway, the town was only a few blocks wide and a few miles long, running north and south, separated from mainland Florida by river and waterway. It was a sleepy little town.

The space age changed that. The sandy spit of land called Cape Canaveral was government owned. Overnight it became America's only launching pad for missiles and space rockets. Industrial firms moved in with new people and new money. Land values shot up to 20 times their original prices and more. It brought new motels, subdivisions, PTAs and schools. Hemmed in by water, builders filled in river bottom to make room for more homes and a hospital.

In a vain attempt at secrecy, the Air Force tried to hide what was going on at the Cape in plain binocular's view of everyone. Inevitably, every bartender and gas station attendant knew the supersecret schedule of coming shots. The details of too many lives were recorded in Air Force security files. In a boomtown atmosphere, where the average age was 25, and where pressures were high, lives often didn't stand close scrutiny. In those early days, the number of divorced men and women in the Cape area was high. Many reputations didn't survive.

Gradually, as the space agency took over and the program matured, the boom subsided somewhat and the towns normalized. The astronauts, often ambitious, aggressive men with passions for fast cars and a fast pace of living, drew the kind of adulation normally reserved for football heroes. That would never change. But when the glamour of Cape Canaveral paled somewhat, the drifters and profit-seekers deserted. In the end, civilization and stability won.

It was apparent from the beginning that the complex programs designed to put men on the moon would need larger quarters, bigger facilities. In July of 1961, just after his space race speech, President Kennedy told officials at the Cape to decide where they would launch the rockets to the moon, and how much land would be needed. He asked for a decision in five days. The officials couldn't make the deadline.

They finally answered three weeks later that the Merritt Island wilderness on the western edge of the space center was the most logical choice. The federal government bought 63,000 additional acres to begin the $49.5-million launch complex for Apollo. In the summer of 1963, the first hole was dug in the island's sand for the launch pad that would hold the Saturn 5 moon rocket.

The manned program was outgrowing its plant at Langley, Va., and at the Cape. After considering some 20 sites around the country, seven of them in Texas, the space agency announced in the fall of 1961 it would build a Manned Spacecraft Center at Houston, Tex. One of the deciding considerations was the gift of a 1,000-acre tract from Rice University. Rice had received it from the Humble Oil and Refining Co. for the express purpose of creating a space research center. Humble retained 33,000 additional acres around the spacecraft center, land that would increase in value in the coming years. In addition, Humble joined Del Webb, a major Southwestern builder, in creating what in essence was a new town, 15,000-acre Clear Lake City. Eventually the space agency purchased 600 more acres from Rice to enlarge the center.

Some found it more than odd that in the competition between sites, Houston had won, when the Vice President and head of the space council was a Texan, as was the chairman of an important subcommittee of the House Appropriations Committee. The latter was Rep. Albert Thomas, now deceased, who took credit for bringing the space center to his constituency. Space agency officials denied there ever was any undue pressure. Nevertheless, the space agency's money requests had to pass through the House committee. A Houston architectural firm, Brown and Root, Inc., won the $1.5-million contract to design the center.

The first half-dozen space agency people were located in a shopping center to begin paving the way for the rest of the staff in late 1961. By July 1, 1962, the entire operation was shifted to temporary quarters in Houston with some 1,640 employes. Only 84 of them refused to transfer. Along with the center came the astronauts as well, locating in fashionable, quite often inexpensive homes in the suddenly bustling communities around the space center. The city of Houston eventually extended its city limits to include the center. By 1966 the staff had grown to nearly 5,000 with a payroll of $50 million annually. By 1963, center employes indicated they would buy some 2,100 homes in the area at a cost of about $36 million. By 1966, the center had active contracts with Texas firms totalling $40.5 million, some $30 million in the Houston area. It was only a drop in the bucket of the $1.5 billion spent by the center indirectly with some 8,000 firms. But it had a remarkable impact on the Houston area.

The space center also drew in more outside money. By August of 1963, over 100 aerospace firms had opened Houston offices to deal with the Manned Spacecraft Center. By 1967 these offices had a payroll of over $4 million. When the space center finally moved out of the dozen or so leased buildings and sheds in southwestern Houston, they moved into what would become a $312-million complex equipped to do everything from checking out and testing spacecraft to guiding flights to the moon. The total cost came to about a third of the cost of Cape Canaveral's launch facilities,

many of which duplicated installations at Houston. The cost of all of the space agency's installations would total over $4.4 billion by mid-1968, 10 years after it all began and a year before men landed on the moon.

At least half a dozen times the space agency selected groups of astronauts, and the selection followed patterns preceding flight by several years. The original seven were largely experimental test pilots. The next groups were flying engineers. The final groups chosen included several scientists, young experts in physics, medicine and other fields that would be important for exploiting space when the machines had been perfected.

But most of the early groups of astronauts gave the collective astronaut his carica-ture, painted him as the daring young man in his flying machine. They entered the program for career reasons, tempered with patriotism and some degree of adventure. Some of them had a sense of advancing science, even the abstract idea of probing the unknown. But largely they were fliers, accustomed to high performance aircraft. On the ground their driving habits became a cause célèbre in the Cape Canaveral area, and for years later, whenever an astronaut was involved in a traffic accident, however innocent, it was attributed to the real or imagined flier's passion for speed.

Without predictable pattern, the astronaut image grew, and the ranks of the origi-nal seven astronauts who had spawned that image, dwindled.

Glenn's friend and fellow astronaut, Scott Carpenter, became a neighborhood hero in 1964 when a young boy threw a metal rake into some power lines trying to free a tangled kite. The power lines shorted and snapped, falling on a metal fence around a backyard where other children were playing. With the children screaming and most

Five Cosmonauts—Pavel Popovich, who tracked down Andrian Nikolayev in space; Alexei Leonov, who was the first man to walk in space; Pavel Belyayev, who was his pilot; Vladimir Komarov, who died in flight; Valentina Tereshkova-Nikolayev, the first woman in space who later married a cosmonaut and bore children.

of the neighbors shocked into immobility, Carpenter and another neighbor quickly measured the situation. While the neighbor used a stick to hold the live wires against a light pole, Carpenter, ignoring the balls of blue flame running up and down the wires, grabbed an axe and chopped them free of the fence.

That same year, assigned to the U.S. Navy's embryo Sealab project to determine how men could live under the seas, Carpenter was hurt. He lost control of a motorbike in an early morning ride on a gravel road near Hamilton, Bermuda. He suffered a badly mangled arm, a severe knee injury and a broken foot. The space agency put him on temporary convalescent duty. But Carpenter would never fly into space again. The injuries from his motorbike accident plagued him through the years. Ultimately, in 1968, they would also cancel his role in the Sealab experiments.

Gordon Cooper liked to race cars, and ran into space agency opposition to his pursuit of the hobby. But almost all of the astronauts drove high-powered sports cars.

In spite of their highway predilections, the very nature of their avocation found them in headlines. Gus Grissom pancake-landed in a kite-like glider, breaking the landing gear, and flew through storm clouds to an emergency landing in a supersonic jet in Florida. "I don't know how I could have gotten down without you," he told traffic controllers later.

Alan Shepard, the first American into space, ran into health troubles less than two years after his flight. It was a problem not uncommon to high altitude flying. A virus settled in his inner ear, causing a condition like Glenn's, dizziness and loss of equilibrium. For that reason, he was grounded in 1963. In 1964, he underwent an operation for a benign tumor on his thyroid gland, and after that became an official in the Astronaut Office, under Slayton, where his training and experience could be helpful with newer astronauts. In 1965, he turned down a request to return to his home state of New Hampshire to run on the Republican ticket for the U.S. Senate. He said he would remain with the space program as long as he could be useful. That same year, at the age of 41, the astronaut who earned $14.38 in flight pay for his 15 minutes in space, became president of the Fidelity Bank and Trust Co. of Houston. For over $2 million, he and two partners bought 52 per cent of the stock of the bank. He also had an interest in another bank in Baytown, Tex.

Fame and the reputations they forged would also lead other astronauts to financial opportunities, some successful and some frank failures. From the newer crop of astronauts, James Lovell and Frank Borman, whose Apollo spaceship first orbited the moon, became members of the boards of directors of banks, Lovell with the LaPorte, Tex., State Bank, and Borman with the Harrisburg, Tex., National Bank. Thomas Stafford and Eugene Cernan, who orbited the moon for 61 hours in Apollo 10, joined as partners in a small Houston air freight business. Other astronauts became advisers to various firms, or consultants on specialty areas of air transportation.

There was sentiment among people who knew the astronauts that they be allowed more financial freedom, allowed to trade on their reputations. There were certainly offers enough. After all, the argument went, these men lived on military or civil service pay and subsisted on meager government per diem allowances while on the road. But they put their lives on the line in space, and their rewards should be commensurate with that.

Ever since the first sale of magazine rights to their personal stories, what the astronaut should or should not be allowed to do financially had been a knotty question. The space agency set up procedures to judge investments and other financial transactions of any important size contemplated by the astronauts. Some astronauts made good investments, some made bad ones. Some became rich and some were no better off than when they started.

The first small group of astronauts reaped something like $16,000 a year from their magazine stories. Following groups, in the growing astronaut corps, had to cut the pie into smaller slices. One estimate in 1969 was that each astronaut got some $3,000 or less from the magazine rights.

At 45, Shepard, already a millionaire, had gone through an expensive, long-term treatment for his ears, had undergone surgery, and was flight-rated again. At 45, Schirra, veteran of three flights from Mercury to Apollo, had decided to leave the program and go to work for a Denver financier named John M. King, who owned a complex of companies which developed mineral and human resources. Schirra became president of one of these, the Regency Investment Corp., and was listed as a director on the board of King's Imperial-American Resources Fund, Inc.

Astronaut Borman was on the board of directors of another King firm, King Resources Co., and was paid some $10,000 a year in that position, company sources said.

Perhaps the most remarkable and tragic chain of events struck the astronaut America had chosen as its greatest hero, John Glenn.

Much of what happened to him after his premier orbital flight in 1962 was predictable. His alma mater, Muskingum College in New Concord, Ohio, gave him the bachelor's degree he missed because of World War II. The space agency was deluged with more than 100,000 fan letters for Glenn, including pennies from children "to help pay for manned space flight" and an offer to name an orchid for him in a flower show. He was beseeched to take free steamship cruises, an all-expense-paid trip to Hawaii, cakes, candies, even an adding machine and an electric computer. Much of it was returned. Cash donations went to charity, including a $100 check from a doctor who said, "You deserve a party. Go out and have a good time."

Glenn's White House meetings with the President led to happy outings at Hyannis Port, Mass., at the Kennedy compound, and to a close association with the President's brother, Robert. Glenn was fond of waterskiing with the Kennedy family and with his own family cruising on the Kennedy yacht, *Marlin*. Indeed, his association with Bobby Kennedy would change his life.

As much as a year after his flight, Glenn was still hoping for a chance to fly in the coming programs of Gemini and Apollo. At the same time there were persistent reports that the Kennedys were trying to get Sen. Stephen Young, 74-year-old Ohio Democrat, to retire, and hoping Glenn would run for Young's Senate seat in 1964.

There were practical reasons for this in the Kennedy political book. Ohio Democrats were pessimistic on John Kennedy's chances for carrying Ohio in 1964. There was a good chance that a national hero like Glenn might not only save the Senate seat for the Democrats, but help the President in his re-election bid. Although his parents were Democrats, Glenn called himself an Independent; said he voted for issues and men, not party. But there was no doubt he liked and admired the Kennedys. Michigan Gov. George Romney, a Republican, and others urged the space hero to run either in New Hampshire or Ohio on the GOP ticket. Glenn countered most of the appeals with his insistence that he would remain in the space program, at least for now.

His lawyer, Leo D'Orsey, announced in September, 1963, that Glenn, who couldn't afford to buy life insurance for his orbital flight, had turned down a job offer that would have paid him a million dollars in 10 years. D'Orsey said the way Glenn felt was, "What can you do for your country?" "I know that sounds corny," the lawyer said. "But it's the way he feels about it."

Whatever made up Glenn's mind, his feeling for the Kennedys was strong, and the events of November 22, 1963, shook him as it did all America. The President was dead. The man who had forged the U.S. space challenge, who had decreed a major effort to reach the moon in this decade, would not be forgotten.

Glenn reassessed his role in the space program. He was now 42. When the United States launched a team to the moon in 1969, he would be 48. No one had said he wouldn't fly again, but space agency officials had indicated that the chances of Apollo flights for the original seven would be slim.

There were also some in the agency who felt that Glenn, as a national hero, should not risk his life on another flight.

In Space And At Sea—Two astronauts get some weightless training aboard space agency planes, and another, Richard Schweickart, learns how to escape from a submerged spacecraft by exiting from an underwater simulator called Dilber the Dunker.

A Band Of Bedouins?—A band of astronauts (from left, front row): Frank Borman, James Lovell, John Young, Charles Conrad, James McDivitt, Edward White; (back row) training officer Ray Zedahar, Thomas Stafford, Donald Slayton, Neil Armstrong, Elliott See. They get desert training in Nevada. Some will see the moon, two will die before the lunar landing, one will never get into space, and one will be the first to set foot on the moon.

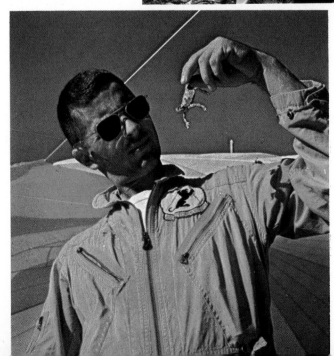

Survival On Earth—Astronauts learn the food value of wild pig and lizards.

Finally, on January 17, 1964, John Glenn decided. He announced he would run for the Democratic nomination for Young's Senate seat that May. Young had already decided to run for re-election. Glenn insisted his conversations with the late President or the President's brother were not overriding in his final judgment. Of the space agency, he said, "It could very well be wishful thinking on my part to train for another six or seven years towards flights for which I might be too old."

Almost from the start, the young and popular astronaut ran ahead of Young in surveys in Ohio. Keeping his home in Houston, he rented an apartment in Columbus, Ohio, to conduct his campaign. Then on February 26, while trying to hang a mirror in the bathroom, he slipped and fell, striking his head against the bathtub. The impact was absorbed by the left side of his head and there was damage to the inner ear, the balance mechanism that provides a sense of equilibrium. It left him with a persistent dizziness. He held on, still in a San Antonio military hospital, until March 30. By then it was apparent to him he would not be able to campaign on the issues. He withdrew from the race. "I did not want to run just as a well-known name," he said. Glenn's name remained on the Ohio ballot even though he took himself out of the race. He had been out of the campaign for the last seven weeks, yet he drew 200,000 votes on election day.

Ailing now and in debt from his foray in the political arena, Glenn faced still more misfortune. With his children about to start college, he found his savings eaten up by his campaign debts. The only politician who extended a helping hand was Robert Kennedy.

Glenn's wife Annie underwent two operations for the successful removal of malignancies. His father fell seriously ill. His father-in-law underwent two brain operations. But for all of that, Glenn's actions did not match his circumstances.

Confined to his home until the dizziness cleared up, he heard that he was up for promotion to colonel in the Marines. It meant a big jump in pay. But because he knew he intended to retire from the service, he asked the promotion board to withdraw his name.

"Sure I would like to be a colonel," he said. "I had been looking forward to being promoted for a long time. But I couldn't see making some poor guy wait another year when I knew I was leaving anyway."

Looking back at the year's events, Glenn said, "There is a luxury in a thing like this being forced upon you. You stop to see where you are going. You pick up all the pieces and start in the direction you feel is best. I am looking forward to the future . . . Next year will be a better year. It's just got to be better than this one."

Things did get better. It took all his savings and 18 months to pay off all his campaign debts. In October he was elected a director of the Royal Crown Cola Co. President Johnson promoted him to colonel anyway, despite his pleas to the contrary. "Here's a man," said the President, "who can orbit the earth and keep Congress on the edge of its seats, but he can't learn to stand up in the bathroom." Glenn's doctors gave him a clean bill of health and cleared him to fly an airplane again. Within a month,

Portrait—Before a mockup capsule, astronauts See, Young, McDivitt, Conrad, Armstrong, and down the ladder, Lovell, White, Borman and Stafford.

he was rolling down the runway at the El Toro, Calif., Marine Base in a red and white jet trainer. He also took on a consultant's job for the space agency. And finally, after 23 years as a Leatherneck, Glenn retired from the Corps on January 4, 1965.

Within a year-and-a-half after joining Royal Crown, Glenn would become vice president in charge of corporate development and later president of Royal Crown International. A close friend of Bobby Kennedy, he would shoot the rapids of the Salmon River with the Kennedy family in 1966, would campaign for Bobby Kennedy in 1968, drawing criticism for his political activity from fellow astronaut Frank Borman. When Robert Kennedy was murdered, it would be John Glenn who would have to tell six of the Kennedy children that their father was dead, and it would be John Glenn who would remain with those children in the days ahead to offer them guidance and soften their grief. And weeks later, it would be John Glenn who would take over as national head of a write-in campaign for stiffer gun-control laws in the Kennedy name.

And months later, of all of the events since 1964, John Glenn would say, "I reached a low point in my life. I've come back from it."

# 7 To Walk In Space

The space fortunes of the United States were changing, too. From the nadir of Sputnik, they rose dramatically, as one economist noted, in direct relation to the amount of money spent. By mid-1965, the United States had spent $8.8 billion on manned space flight, and its total expenditures on space since Sputnik reached some $14.4 billion.

The space agency which began with a handful of men now employed 33,200 on its own staff and almost 377,000 in outside firms, not counting the employes in thousands of companies working on space agency projects full or part-time. The Mercury program was over, and the agency looked back and figured that at its peak more than two million people had a hand in sending the six astronauts into space, at a cost of $384 million.

Now, the U.S. space effort entered its second stage. It would fly the two-man Gemini spaceship, a maneuverable craft that was designed to change orbit, while other experts built and designed the three-man Apollo ships that would fly in 1968 and 1969.

In less than two years beginning in the spring of 1965, the United States was to reach a position of dominance in the space race for the first time, and Americans would be standing on the launch pad where they could almost reach the moon, but not quite.

In the same two years there would be renewed criticism of the space race as too expensive, as a foolhardy adventure into the skies when man's real troubles of poverty and ignorance were down on earth. In the careful, plodding step-by-step answer to the Soviet challenge, many Americans would become bored by the sameness of space flights, so frequent and regular that they had all the excitement of takeoffs and landings at a local airport. Many would gripe when space flight news interfered with sports events or favorite programs on television. It seemed that the people who were paying the bill were losing interest at the very moment when they were winning the space race.

The Russians were not flying as often, perhaps for economy's sake. They were undoubtedly benefiting from the open information available from U.S. flights. And they were still doing things first in space.

A month after Cooper's flight, the Soviets repeated their feat of orbiting two spacecraft into nearly parallel circles around the earth. But this time somebody new had been added. On June 14, 1963, Vostok V dashed into orbit with Vladimir Bykovsky aboard, a routine flight. Two days later, Vostok VI flew into orbit and surprised the world. There was a woman at the controls. Valentina Tereshkova became the first female into space. Before the two returned to earth three days later, the spaceships passed within three miles of each other, within easy sight, while the world wondered why the Russians had orbited a woman, and one who was not a pilot at that. Valentina Tereshkova was an experienced parachutist, but not a trained flier.

In time, the most logical reasons seemed to be the obvious ones. First, the five-ton Vostok spacecraft, for all its size, was not maneuverable and could not change orbit, so piloting ability was not essential. The second reason seemed to be Soviet curiosity as to whether a woman, with her somewhat different biological functions, could endure space flight as well as a man. Valentina Tereshkova apparently answered that in the affirmative. She later married another veteran Vostok pilot, Nikolayev, and the pair produced healthy children, disposing of any concern that there could be radiation damage to genes in near-earth orbit. The married space couple also became a popular public showpiece of Soviet prowess in space, an idea which might have also entered into Soviet flight plans.

In the spring of 1964, a year after Cooper's flight, the United States successfully tested both a dummy Gemini spacecraft and a dummy Apollo, neither with a man aboard. In the fall of 1964, without prior notice, the Russians flew the world's first three-man space team into orbit, aboard Voshkod—Sunrise I—with a doctor, Boris Yegorov, a scientist, Konstantin Feoktistov, and a pilot, Col. Vladimir Komarov. Komarov would become the first Soviet cosmonaut to fly twice. But his efforts would end in tragedy for Soviet space experts.

The Voshkod I flight apparently gave the Soviets pause with their new spacecraft because of recurrent nausea reported by the crew. The premiere flight ended after 16 orbits.

Six months later, another Voshkod spaceship flew into orbit to provide the world with another first, and a thrill it would never forget. Leaving pilot Pavel Belyayev behind in the cockpit, Soviet cosmonaut Alexei Leonov opened the hatch and took that first awful step into the nothingness of space. For 10 minutes, he maneuvered around by himself, alone with the stars, the sun and the moon, a human satellite testing whether man dared to work in this hostile environment, protected only by a spacesuit from forces that would mean instant destruction for the human body.

The two-year moratorium on U.S. manned flights after Mercury did not mean launch crews were idle at Cape Canaveral, now renamed Cape Kennedy, nor at Vandenberg Air Force Base on the Pacific coast. Both the United States and the Soviet Union kept up the steady rumble of rocket firings, sending unmanned satellites of

First Spacewalker—Cosmonaut Alexei Leonov looked back and saw his spaceship as a lonely planet on a shoreless ocean.

every description into orbit. Coupled with the scientific satellites sent up by the space agency were scores of military satellites probing new ways of communicating and spying from space.

By the time Gemini was ready to fly, the United States had fired more than 250 satellites into space, compared to 112 for the Soviet Union. No one knew how many Soviet failures there had been, but the American batting average was plain to see, and it was improving. In 1957, one try, one failure. In 1958, 17 tries, 10 failures. In 1959, 19 tries, eight failures. In 1960, 29 tries, 13 failures. In 1961, 41 tries, 12 failures. In 1962, 59 tries, seven failures. In 1963, 45 tries, eight failures. In 1964, 59 tries, five failures. In 1965, 68 tries, six failures.

But in manned flight, most space agency officials conceded that the Soviet Union had a two-year lead in early 1965, still capitalizing on a booster rocket three times the power of the Titan that would hurl Gemini into orbit.

Less than a week after Leonov's space walk and the Soviet's return to earth in an off-target landing that ended up in a snowbank, the United States flew two men for the first time. Gus Grissom and space rookie John W. Young, after a year of training, tested the Gemini 3 spacecraft for three orbits, used maneuvering rockets to lower their altitude and nudge the spaceship from side to side, changing their path around the earth. They splashed down 60 miles short of target because wind tunnel tests did not give the experts a proper reading on how much lift the spacecraft would develop during re-entry. Grissom, still stung by suggestions that his error may have been responsible for sinking his Liberty Bell spaceship during the Mercury program, called his new Gemini ship "The Unsinkable Molly Brown." Even then the spacecraft splashed down with so much impact it went under water, then righted itself and bobbed up again. Young, a 34-year-old Navy lieutenant commander who once lectured his 11th grade class on rocketry, was left speechless by his first launch into space. "You can't take your eyes from the window," he said. "There aren't words in the English language to describe the sight."

Grissom's only real troubles were seasickness as the Molly Brown pitched in the turbulent sea, and an illicit corned beef sandwich the crew smuggled aboard and he ate in space. It brought orders from space agency headquarters to stop all contraband on space flights. Nearing his 39th birthday, Grissom was the first American to fly into space twice. For his mother in his hometown of Mitchell, Ind., it was a tense experience. Perhaps it was premonition. "It's on my nerves terribly," she said. "I think it's worse this time . . . If I had known when Virgil was a little boy he would be flirting with danger in space, I would probably have died." Grissom would be chosen as command pilot for the first test of the three-man Apollo spaceship in the racing years to come and he was to be the first American to blast off into space three times.

What Gemini 3 lacked in spectacle, Gemini 4 more than made up for. On June 3, on the third orbit of their four-day flight, astronaut Edward Higgins White II took leave of his command pilot, James A. McDivitt, stepped out into space to see sights and feel thrills only one man had encountered before him.

Around him, cold and black, the empty reaches of space offered no real notion of distance, save for the glimmering stars, the sun blazing with the blinding white flame of a welder's torch, and nearer, more gentle, the lonely quarter moon, soft and small. Thus did White, age 35, father of two, become a would-be planet in orbit around the earth. Clad in a $28,000 spacesuit to protect him, White was in a perpetual fall around the planet he called home, hurtling at 17,500 miles an hour but without any sense of speed. His only ties to reality were the crackling voices beamed by radio into his helmet, and the golden tether that coiled through the blackness to the gleaming white spaceship behind him. The American flag on his left shoulder seemed alive, catching the rays of the sun, and there was no face visible in the mirror-like visor that protected his eyes from the searing light. Below, the earth's blanket of air caught the sun's white light and shattered it into colors. The earth itself stretched out like some brilliant plain, a great montage in turquoise, brown, gold and purple, stark under white clouds.

White used a small oxygen-spitting gun to maneuver around his ship in a weightless world where the only laws are laws of motion, and every action has its equal and opposite reaction, every tug moves both the tugger and the tugged. White's lean, 170-pound body could move the 7,500-pound spaceship, like a man leading a large dog on a leash.

"One thing about it, when Ed gets out there and starts wiggling around, it sure makes the spacecraft tough to control," McDivitt reported to earth.

They maneuvered around for each other, each of them taking pictures. "Let me take a close-up picture here," McDivitt requested. Then as White's unreal image pressed closer, McDivitt laughed, "Hey, you're smearing my windshield, you dirty dog."

Time flew by the two astronauts, as Grissom radioed up from the ground repeatedly trying to get an answer from them. They were flying over Texas at the time looking down at Houston and Galveston Bay, talking about pictures. Grissom persisted. Finally he raised McDivitt. "The flight director says 'get back in,'" Grissom said. "Got any messages for us?" McDivitt asked. "Gemini 4, get back in," Grissom said urgently. "Okay," McDivitt said, but he reckoned without his space-walking copilot.

"I'm fine," said White. "No," McDivitt said, "back in, come on."

White's laughing voice was garbled as heard on the ground. "I'm not coming in," he said. "We've got three-and-a-half more days to go," McDivitt insisted. "Come on, let's get back in here before it gets dark."

"Okay, I'm fixing to come in the house," White said. But it was slow going and difficult to move without hand-holds and foot-holds in weightless space. Ultimately, White slipped into his seat, much to the relief of Grissom and other ground controllers. Then the first American spacewalker turned to his pilot and said, "It's the saddest moment of my life." McDivitt laughed.

Later when McDivitt was sleeping, White talked to Grissom about the space walk. "Hey, Ed," Grissom asked, "you talked about walking on that spaceship. Were you actually walking on it?"

Second Spacewalker—
Astronaut Ed White,
would-be human satellite
of earth, has the view
of a lifetime, smears a
windshield, tugs at the
spacecraft, kids about
not coming back in. He
carried three religious
medallions with him. In
1967, he dies on a
land-locked spacecraft
with two other astronauts
in a tragedy that almost
halts the U.S. race to
the moon.

"Yes, I was," White replied. "I was using the tether to pull myself down on the spacecraft. It looked like I was right on top of it, as a matter of fact. It's kind of hard to get traction on top, but when you pull yourself down, you do get a little bit."

So the conversation went between them. In less than two years, sitting side-by-side with rookie astronaut Roger Chaffee in the first Apollo spaceship, they would die together in America's first spacecraft accident.

As the flight progressed, there was little for the astronauts to do. Their wives were brought into Gemini Control to talk to them via radio, and urged them to drink more water and get more sleep. "It looked like you were having a wonderful time yesterday," Pat White said to her husband. "Quite a time, quite a time," he replied. When he returned to earth, White said he had no feeling of fear, only a sense of accomplishment. "I felt quite natural out there," he said. And it stood in contrast to the poetic images that cosmonaut Alexei Leonov saw, looking back at his Voshkod spacecraft. To him, he said, the spacecraft was a planet, a lonely planet on a shoreless ocean.

Interestingly, White was not recorded as a satellite. He wasn't in orbit long enough, his 20-minute space walk falling some 70 minutes short of an orbit. They did record the glove he lost in space as item No. 1,392. The Air Force Spacetrack Center at Colorado Springs, Colo., which keeps tab of such things, listed Gemini 4 as the 1,390th object in orbit, and its rocket booster was listed as No. 1,391. With Gemini 4 in orbit were 600 other satellites or space debris tracked by Air Force radar.

Both White, a Methodist, and McDivitt, a Roman Catholic, paid homage to their faith in space. White on his space walk carried three medallions—a St. Christopher medal, a gold cross and a Star of David. "I couldn't take one for every religion in the country, but I took the three I perhaps was the most familiar with." Later in Rome, McDivitt was asked to comment on a Soviet cosmonaut's statement that he could not see a trace of God in space. "I did not see God looking into my space cabin window, as I did not see God looking into my car's windshield on earth," McDivitt replied. "But I could recognize His work in the stars as well as when walking among the flowers in a garden. If you can be with God on earth, you can be with God in space . . ."

The theme of the devout astronaut echoed through many U.S. flights. On the edge

Astronaut's Wife—
Marilyn Lovell and sons
watch James Lovell ride
a Titan rocket into space
in Gemini 7.

of the moon, it would provide the American people with one of the most moving moments of the space race.

Oddly, the U.S. space programs were named for the pagan gods of Greek mythology, Gemini for the constellation that ancient astronomers thought looked like two men sitting side-by-side. The two brightest stars in Gemini were named for Castor and Pollux, the twin sons of Zeus. McDivitt and White were close not only as crewmates but as friends and schoolmates at the University of Michigan, where both received degrees in 1959, McDivitt his bachelors as first in a class of 606, and White his masters as seventh in his class.

If U.S. space progress influenced the pattern of Soviet flights, then the McDivitt-White flight was evidence the United States could be copycat too. U.S. officials hadn't planned a space walk until Gemini 6. But after Leonov's excursion, they changed their plans to include a 10-to-12-minute walk for White. What President Johnson had intimated earlier was a stunt in Soviet plans became the centerpiece of the Gemini 4 flight.

There were two small incidents that touched the Gemini 4 flight, but reached beyond it to political questions that would eventually affect the future of the space program. Each was a symptom of concern and argument that would congeal in America in the years ahead. First, during the flight, white and Negro pickets appeared near the Manned Spacecraft Center to protest what they called unyielding segregation in Houston schools. One sign read, "Space Age City, Stone Age Schools." And at the University of Michigan's Student Union, the astronauts were ushered in a back door to avoid student pickets on the front steps protesting the war in Vietnam. When the space program finally reached the moon in 1969, the cost of the war in Vietnam and the plight of the Negro in America would become major factors in budget reductions for the space program, and at least temporary limitations on its future.

In August of 1965, the rapid pace of Gemini flights did what it set out to do. It eclipsed Soviet-held world records, gave the United States its first real leadership in the manned space race. Two of the smallest astronauts, Gordon Cooper at 5-feet-8 and Charles Conrad Jr. at 5-feet-6, rode a devil-plagued Gemini 5 spaceship through eight days of what Cooper called cliff-hanging, never sure their flight would not be cut off, never sure what would go wrong next.

To insure the United States would get credit, an official who would propose the records to international archives first placed two $1 bills aboard the Gemini 5 spaceship before launch, and then waited aboard the prime recovery ship, the carrier *Lake Champlain,* in the Atlantic for Gemini 5's return. Then he would compare the serial numbers of the bills. The oddity was part of the international regulations concerning records and safeguards against falsification. John Glenn carried a driver's license for that purpose aboard Friendship 7, and Alan Shepard carried a Confederate bill on the first venture into space.

By the time Gemini 5 splashed down, it had entered these world records in the United States column: longest manned space flight—190 hours, 56 minutes, breaking the old record of 119 hours and six minutes set by Soviet Lt. Col. Valery Bykovsky; total man-hours in space—639 hours, 48 minutes set by 12 astronauts in nine U.S. flights, breaking the old record of 507 hours, 16 minutes set by 11 cosmonauts in eight flights; most orbits in space—120, breaking Bykovsky's mark of 81; individual with most orbits and most flight time—Gordon Cooper, the first man to make two orbital flights, compiling 225 hours and 15 minutes in 142 orbits, topping Bykovsky's single flight total.

All eyes were on the spacecraft clock when the moment approached and the first Russian record was fading away. Chris Kraft, a man who doesn't like to fly himself but who "flies" every minute of every mission from the flight director's console, stared intently at the seconds clicking away. As it passed the magic mark, he grinned and shouted, "Zap!" Later he took the microphone to ask Cooper how it felt for the United States to be a world record holder. The slow Oklahoma drawl came back from space, "At last, huh?"

Yet oddly enough, there were signs of boredom with the whole thing among the people who had paid for the race from the beginning. The American public, for whatever mood or reason, seemed to be rebelling, or at least some of it was. Columbia Broadcasting System, which broadcast seven hours of an attempted launch of Gemini 5 that ended in a scrub, rued its "mistake." Then, when the spaceship ran into trouble on the first day of its mission and was in danger of being brought down early, CBS received 521 calls in New York and Philadelphia protesting the interruption of scheduled football games. The National Broadcasting Co. caught 250 protesting calls in Washington, also for interrupting a football game to telecast reports on Gemini 5 troubles.

Whether it spoke for only ardent football fans, or for most Americans, it was a symptom of public apathy that was to grow worse before it changed.

Not everyone could feel the excitement that 26-year-old Jerry Bostick felt. He was making his debut as officer in charge of the launch. His heartbeat recorded by flight surgeons was the highest rate in the Gemini Control room—150 beats a minute. Even the astronauts were cooler. Veteran space flier Cooper had a heart rate of only 135, and rookie Conrad had 145, riding the roaring Titan rocket into space. There was $3 in the "cool pool" in Gemini Control. The winner was Chris Kraft, with a heart rate of 105. Barred from the pool because of too many previous wins was flight surgeon Charles Berry with a heart rate of 85, nearly normal.

Cooper and Conrad never lost their cool, despite a series of troubles with fuel supplies, power systems, and finally venting gases that set their spacecraft into an annoying tumble. Their early orbits were so filled with work they lost sleep because of it. Their later orbits, tumbling and conserving fuel, were so idle they had little to do but sleep and listen to broadcast music like "Fly Me To The Moon," and trade nonsense poems with the ground below. They talked briefly via radio to Scott Carpenter, the astronaut-turned-aquanaut. Carpenter was in Sealab 2, resting on the ocean floor, 205 feet down off the coast of California. He traded good wishes with Gemini 5, more than 100 miles up in space.

Once again, the men in the machines had proved they could overcome severe problems in space. Six of the nine U.S. manned flights had faced trouble, three of them so serious that the pilots had to overcome the difficulties or the mission would have failed. The Gemini 5 mission joined that list. Said flight director Kraft, "If it had been an unmanned vehicle, I doubt that we would have gotten it back."

There was one unusual footnote to the Gemini 5 story. Off on a two-week goodwill tour of Europe, Cooper and Conrad encountered Soviet cosmonauts Alexei Leonov and Pavel Belyayev in Athens. Each pair bypassed their official guides, embraced and later sat down to breakfast together. Toasting the Soviets, Cooper said, "You're just like us. We love to fly. You love to fly."

Just after the Gemini 5 pilots returned from tour, the United States was set to launch Gemini 6, a hunter spacecraft which would track down and mate with an orbiting rocket engine to be sent into space first. It was a more sophisticated attempt to do an experiment that failed on Gemini 5 because of spacecraft trouble. But this one failed, too. The target rocket broke apart six minutes after it was launched, and Wally Schirra, ready for his second flight, and Thomas Stafford, set for his first, were stopped hours short of blastoff.

Flight experts huddled over what to do. They needed the experience of chasing down another object in the sky, needed a target for Gemini 6 to test its radar and computers on. They finally came up with a change in flight plans that was to provide one of the most spectacular shows in the Gemini series. Gemini 7, with rookies Frank Borman and James Lovell aboard, was scheduled for a 14-day marathon ride in orbit in December. Why not use Gemini 7 as the target for Gemini 6? The only problem was that both would blastoff from the same Launch Pad 19. Could the inevitable damage to the pad caused by the Gemini launch be repaired in time to get Gemini 6 up and counting for the space hunt? Normally it took launch pad crews as much as two months to repair damage to the pad and set up a new shot. This time they did it in eight days.

Gemini 7 began its lonely duty as an orbiting target without trouble. Borman and Lovell filled their early days in space taking pictures, adjusting their flight path with small bursts of rocket power, and listening to music beamed up from earth. Among the musical items were lyrics like "I'll be home for Christmas," "Going home to Houston, Houston, Houston," and "Stayed around this lonesome town too long—and I feel like I gotta travel on."

Meanwhile on earth, the Gemini 6 crew rehearsed the maneuvers that would enable it to track down Gemini 7 in the skies. Schirra and Stafford went through simulated flight after simulated flight, perfecting timing and calculations. Told of the preparations below, Lovell kidded, "Roger, we just passed over the Cape and with our telescope we could see them working down there."

As preparations sped on, Gemini 6 got a go-ahead early, and Gemini 7 was told to change its egg-shaped orbit to a full circle in preparation. "We'll try to fit it into our schedule," Borman said with a smile in his voice.

Gemini 7 was racing over Cape Kennedy when the countdown for Gemini 6 clicked

While Gemini 6 waited for blastoff the first time, only Schirra's cool nerve prevented disaster. Later they shot into space on time.

to zero. The rocket ignited, but then just as suddenly shut down. Schirra and Stafford were helpless, sitting atop the hot Titan rocket. An automatic system had sensed something wrong and cut the rocket off before it left the pad. Only cool thinking on the part of command pilot Wally Schirra saved the mission for another day. He sat in the cockpit with a D-ring in his hand. Had he pulled it, he and Stafford would have been ejected from the spacecraft, shooting to a safe distance away from the loaded rocket. He decided to chance sitting tight until launch experts diagnosed the trouble. It turned out to be minor and the launch was rescheduled for a later day, still aiming for rendezvous with Gemini 7. But if Schirra had panicked and pulled the ejection mechanism, it would have blown all chances of a two-spacecraft flight. And it could have left both astronauts injured, since ejection at the pad is at low altitude and a truly desperate move to escape an exploding rocket.

Flight experts quickly revamped the launch schedule, ordered orbiting Gemini 7 into drifting flight to save fuel, and set up a new countdown for Gemini 6. Said Wally Schirra: "Tell Frank and Jim that we still want to come up and see them."

The launch area was blanketed by fog on the mornings approaching the next try. But the sun came through and burned it away. Finally, on the third try, the engines of the Titan roared into life and Gemini 6 drilled its way into space in hot pursuit of the bearded and tired astronauts of Gemini 7. With Gemini 6 doing all the maneuvering, and Gemini 7 loafing through its last days, the pilots provided the running commentary. "We didn't get to see the liftoff," said Lovell in Gemini 7, "but we saw them coming up through the clouds." Told the steering looked good, Schirra in Gemini 6 said, "Oh, she looks like a dream." In less than four hours, Gemini 6 had Gemini 7 in radar contact, tweaking its jet engines to move into the circular orbit. Then came the report from Stafford in Gemini 6, "We're about 120 feet and sitting."

"It's great . . . really outstanding," said Lovell in Gemini 7.

As they moved to a few feet and grinned at each other through their spacecraft windows, Schirra said, "You're up close."

"I can see your lips moving," said Lovell in Gemini 7.

"I'm chewing gum," said Schirra in Gemini 6.

"Can you see Frank's beard, Wally?" asked Lovell.

"I can see yours better right now," said Schirra.

"There seems to be a lot of traffic up here," said Schirra. "Call a policeman," suggested Borman.

"How's the visibility?" asked Lovell. "It's pretty bad," said Schirra. "I see through the window and see you fellows inside."

For a change too, space pilots could see themselves as others would see them. Gemini 7 dumped some waste water through one of its vents. It hit the cold of space and froze. "You've got a real ball of ice behind you," said Schirra from next door. He also pointed out some loose wires or straps hanging from Gemini 7, explaining strange slapping noises they heard early in flight. Gemini 7 told Schirra that he had some too. They photographed each other for posterity.

Zeroing In—Gemini 6 tracks down Gemini 7, and the two fly in formation around the earth.

Schirra later admitted a twinge of remorse when he had to coax his spaceship away from Gemini 7. "See you in a couple of days," he said. Then, in the silence of his craft, sitting next to Stafford, he could not help thinking that this had been a great moment on the way to the moon, something that had to be done to prove it could be done, and the four of them had done it.

Gemini 6 splashed down on December 16 after a little more than 26 hours in space. On the morning of December 18, after a spaghetti breakfast squeezed from one of the plastic food tubes, the Gemini 7 pilots splashed down, too. They had entered another 330 hours and 35 minutes in the U.S. space log. It more than doubled the total U.S. man-hours in space to nearly 1,345, a mark the Soviets would never match before the moon landing.

It seemed as though the United States had a clear lead in manned flight now. It had also orbited some 300 unmanned satellites to 150 for the Soviets. But all this could be viewed critically. As one expert put it, the United States was putting up twice as many satellites as the Soviet Union, but continues to fall behind each year in the weight of the payload orbited. Both Soviet manned and unmanned craft weighed more than American ships. They still had bigger rockets and they were using them.

"We're pursuing a course that we hope will provide the United States with leadership," said Dr. George E. Mueller, chief of manned space flight, earlier. "I don't think one flight or achievement is going to determine leadership in space. The flights over the long term will provide us with a sound basis for leadership."

But Chris Kraft, shepherd of U.S. flights, thought of it as a race between the Soviet Union as the hare, the United States as the tortoise. "When we do pass him, we will astound ourselves at what we can accomplish," he said.

Hunters Home From The Hill—Schirra and Stafford splashed down in the Pacific after their space hunt and formation flight with Gemini 7.

Grand Central Station—
New York crowds watch
the first manned Gemini
launch. The "Unsinkable
Molly Brown" returned
home safely. But there
was trouble ahead.

# 8 Twenty Men In Twenty Months

The moon, pale and passive, mindless, scarred by supreme violence, orbited the earth as it had for ages, remote; as one saw it in the heavens, "a ruined world, a globe burnt out, a corpse upon the road of night."

From the moon, the earth was only a cloud-whipped turquoise sphere rising over its cratered, mountained horizon. Yet the future of these primeval lunar rocks was being changed by the bustling of a million creatures a quarter of a million miles away —too small and too distant to see.

On the earth, in 1966, it seemed possible that the United States could make its self-imposed deadline. It was almost acceptable to the mind that an American would, before the decade was done, stand on the moon's ruined surface. And if the mind accepted that, it dared the question, which American? Whose foot would first press the lunar soil? Whose name would live with history?

He was one of those flying now. Gemini, the experimental two-man spaceship, did what it set out to do: hurl 20 men into space in just 20 months. The flights clicked away like a dreary metronome in the affairs of men. Cape Kennedy had all the glamour of a local airport. Houston was merely a control tower monitoring flight. Or so it seemed.

Of course, Gemini was much more than it seemed. It was the crucible to test the idea of flying to the moon, to wring out the way to do it from success and mistake, to forge the men who would make the voyage. And one day, one man from among these men would be chosen to be the ultimate explorer, the first to stand on a foreign celestial body and look back on earth.

Yet so great was the gap between the idea and the reality that in 1966 the moon remained an image in the sky and on computer paper. There was much more real work to be done on earth. The moonport at Cape Kennedy was under construction. The rockets were under test at Huntsville. In a thousand conferences in factories and laboratories, the road maps and the spacecraft designs were probed and argued. And the men were learning, and there was so much to learn. Nothing was without hazard.

In the course of preparing for flights, astronauts and their backup teams kept a careful eye on the systems that would carry them into space. As they all knew, as John Glenn remembered, experience was confidence.

On February 28, the crew and the backup crew for Gemini 9, scheduled to blast off at mid-year, flew from Texas to St. Louis to check out their spaceship at the McDonnell Aircraft plant where it was being built. Astronauts Elliot M. See Jr. and Charles Bassett flew the lead plane with the backup crew, Tom Stafford and Eugene A. Cernan, in the second jet flying formation at its wingtip.

Weather reports along the way told of light rain, snow and fog, but acceptable ceilings and visibility at Lambert Field. See, piloting the first plane, broke through the clouds and came over the centerline of the runway, but too high for a straight-in approach. He decided to make a circle below the clouds, relying on his eyes, without radio approach aids. As he went into his turning bank, the plane began to lose altitude, too rapidly. When it glanced off the roof of the McDonnell building, it was nose up and struggling to build up thrust. Seventeen persons were hurt at that first impact. See and Bassett were killed when their aircraft exploded in flames in a parking lot nearby.

Stafford and Cernan lost sight of the lead plane while making the circle. Stafford requested a radar approach and landed 14 minutes after the crash. Officials later blamed poor visibility and weather reports that did not match the weather as the cause. Ironically, some 500 feet from where See and Bassett crashed, their spacecraft was undergoing checks by McDonnell technicians. Now Stafford and Cernan were pressed into Gemini 9 duties.

See and Bassett were the second and third astronauts killed in the space program. Theodore Freeman was killed in a training plane crash near Houston on October 31, 1964.

The crash did not slow Gemini's pace appreciably. Gemini 8 was set for a March launch. Its pilot was Neil Armstrong, a 35-year-old civilian who as a naval pilot flew 78 combat missions in Korea, a Purdue graduate who earned his test pilot wings with the old NACA, flying the X-15 rocket plane. He was the first civilian to fly an American spacecraft. His copilot was Air Force Lt. Col. David R. Scott, son of a retired Air Force general, fifth in his class at West Point, married to the daughter of another retired Air Force general.

What had gone wrong repeatedly for Gemini 6, worked perfectly for Armstrong and Scott in Gemini 8. Right on schedule, the launch experts at Cape Kennedy shot an Agena target rocket into space. Less than two hours later Armstrong and Scott roared off in pursuit of the target. They were to track it down, test out the Agena, and later give Scott a chance at a world record two-hour walk in space.

After watching the perfect twin launching, President Johnson said, "We are going to be the first to land a man on the moon, and we will land him in the 1960s." Armstrong, told the Agena was in a good orbit, said, "Beautiful. We'll take that one."

Both were guilty of premature optimism. Armstrong, at the controls of Gemini 8, gently nudged the spaceship toward the Agena. After a 105,000-mile chase, he and

On The Way To Rendezvous—Gemini 10 blasts off in a multiple exposure shot that shows the gantry going down and the rocket going up.

Scott coasted up to the fuel-laden target rocket, sometimes called a flying bomb in space. They docked with it, inserting the nose of the Gemini 8 into the nose collar of the Agena. It was the first time two spacecraft had ever docked together in space.

But about half an hour later—out of radio contact with Gemini tracking stations, over the heartland of China—Scott noticed that the joined spacecraft and rocket were beginning to move strangely, straying out of position. Armstrong struggled to control it, to little avail. It got worse with time.

Finally in radio contact again, Armstrong beamed to earth, "We have serious trouble here. We're tumbling end over end."

Almost Ready And Waiting—Cape Kennedy's moonport complex, dominated by the Vehicle Assembly Building in the center, a crawler-trailer for moving Saturn 5 rockets at the right, and the launch pad in the distant center. While Gemini flew, they built the launch pads for the mission to the moon.

The two pilots, their voices crisp but calm, said they felt like they were in a spinning airplane, and at times the movement was so severe they couldn't read their instrument panels overhead. They didn't feel as if they would black out, but "it's rolling," said Armstrong, "and we can't turn anything off."

At first Armstrong thought there was trouble with the Agena, that one of its control jets had gone haywire. Afraid the wild gyrations would break the spacecraft apart, he used his vital control system normally reserved for returning to earth to push away from the Agena. But that didn't solve the problem either. It was a thruster on the spacecraft that had gone haywire, and Gemini 8 was still tumbling through space.

Flight director John Hodge in Gemini Control asked in his soft British accent, "We're interested in the position of the Agena . . . particularly if it's in front or behind."

But communications were not the best either. Hodge persisted, "Gemini 8, do you have any idea where the Agena is?"

"No, we don't," came Armstrong's terse reply.

A tracking station finally found it, and measured by radio its relative position to Gemini 8. The Agena was some 120 miles away, in front and below the two astronauts. There didn't seem to be any way to control Gemini 8's tumbling without expending valuable fuel. There was no way to save the mission. Armstrong and Scott were ordered to make an emergency landing in the Pacific Ocean. On its seventh trip around, what began as a perfect flight came to a scary but safe ending. Gemini 8 was spotted by an Air Force rescue plane as it descended by parachute. Three hours after splashdown the astronauts and their spacecraft were picked up by the destroyer *USS Mason*. What had been intended as a 71-hour mission loaded with world records ended short of the 14-hour mark, and all because of a short circuit that triggered a control jet. Man was not yet the master of space flight.

Gemini was sending up a lot of spacecraft, and much had been learned. But one critical element was missing in terms of real experience—docking. Several times the Agena target rocket had failed to orbit. When Gemini 8 docked it could remain hooked up for only some 30 minutes. The space agency set to work on a substitute for the target Agena. Experts built what they called an Augmented Target Docking Adapter, shorter than the Agena, and minus the rocket engine. But it could be used if Agena failed, and it would provide the needed experience in docking, undocking and redocking.

This was a vital link on the way to the moon. The Apollo moonship would have to dock with the small space taxi that would take two of the crewmen to the lunar surface. In orbit around the moon, the comparatively fragile and lightweight taxi would land on the moon, then blast off again to rendezvous and dock with the mother ship still in orbit around the moon. If the men in the lunar lander had trouble, the mother ship would have to rescue it, again docking with it. Without a proven ability to rendezvous and dock, without men trained in the maneuvers, there would be no trip to the moon. Said a sign on Chris Kraft's desk: "Rendezvous is hard."

Stafford was a rendezvous veteran from the twin flights of Gemini 6 and 7. Now he, and a space rookie, Gene Cernan, would fly Gemini 9. After the rendezvous and docking with an Agena rocket, Cernan was set for a two-hour, 35-minute space walk, first on a short tether, then on a longer one with a portable maneuvering unit he would wear on his back, a la Buck Rogers. It was an ambitious, busy flight plan, little more than two days long.

As if that weren't enough, it was also the 13th manned space flight on the U.S. calendar. The first thing that failed was the Agena. Radio contact was lost with the target vehicle eight minutes after launch and it plunged into the sea. This time the space agency was ready with a substitute, the new ATDA. Two days after the target was

The "Angry Alligator"—Stafford and Cernan rode Gemini 9 to a rendezvous with their target in the sky—but they found it with its shroud still on, agape like the jaws, said Stafford, of an "angry alligator."

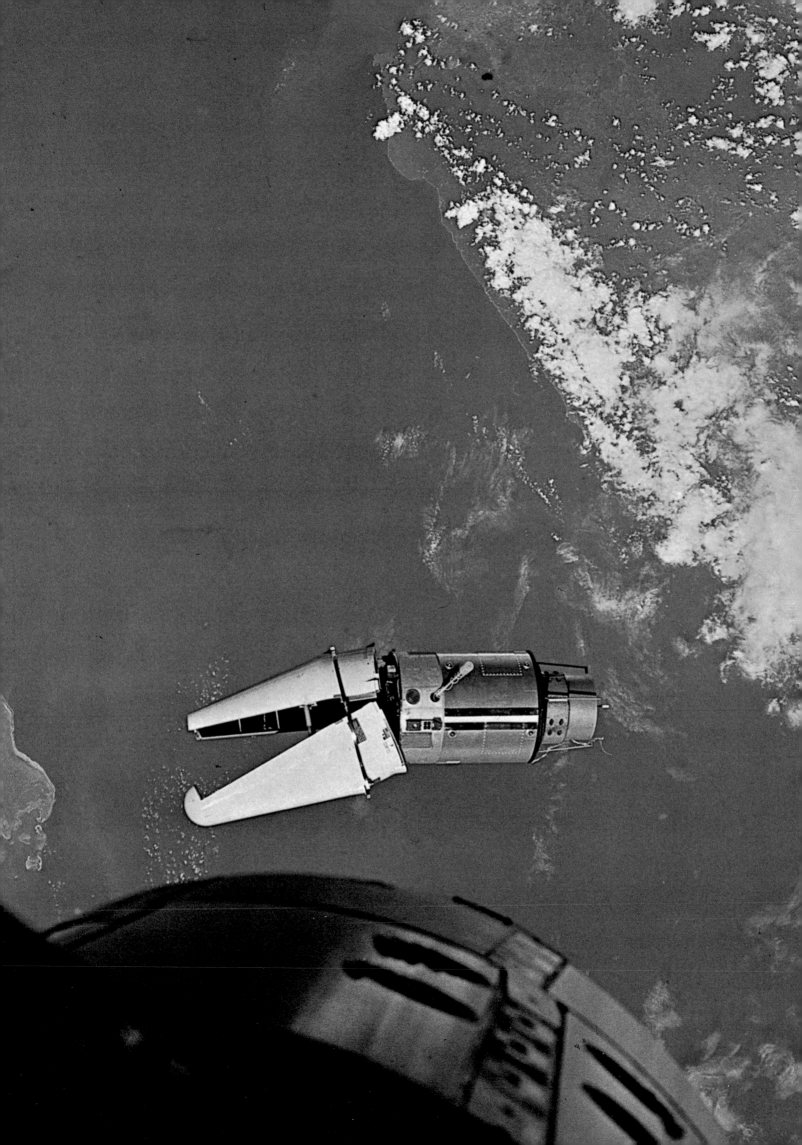

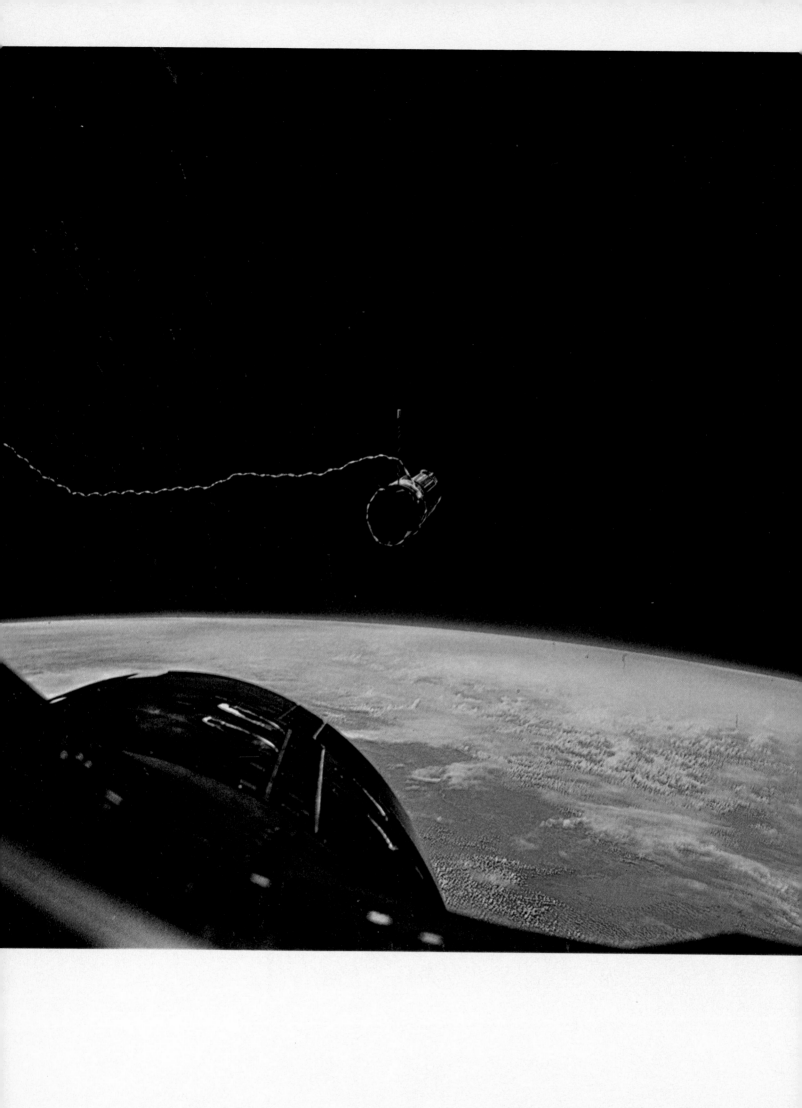

launched, Stafford and Cernan ripped into orbit in pursuit of it. At the end of a 75,000-mile chase, they spotted its red running lights two-and-a-half miles away. "We're looking right into the moon," Stafford reported. "This should be interesting."

It was at least that. When they finally caught up with the flying barrel, they found it still wearing the spun-glass shroud that was to protect it during launch. The shroud was partly agape. It looked, said Stafford, like the open jaws of "an angry alligator."

Repeatedly, by radio command, flight experts tried to shake the shroud loose. They were not successful. Later they discovered the disconnect devices were only taped on instead of being firmly fastened. "We have a weird looking machine," Stafford said.

Docking was obviously stymied again. But flight designers set Stafford and Scott to running difficult rendezvous exercises with their "alligator," backing off and chasing it down from above. It was hard work. They kept losing the target in the glare of the earth's oceans, clouds and land masses. It proved the necessity of radar in rendezvous plans. But it also cost a lot of maneuvering fuel, and left the astronauts exhausted. "We're pretty well bushed," Stafford reported. "It raises a question in my own mind whether and when the EVA [space walk] should be done. Perhaps we should wait until tomorrow morning."

It was well that they did. Cernan, struggling in the restraint of the pressurized spacesuit and trying to perform a number of chores, grew progressively more tired. His heart was beating some 180 a minute with exertion. He could talk only with Stafford. "Boy, is it beautiful out there, Tom," Cernan said as he stuck his head out through the hatch. But after that his voice betrayed his effort as he tried to pull himself along by handrails not well spaced on the ship's hull. He also had to avoid the jet thrusters that controlled the position of the spacecraft. "Strange world out here, you know it?" he asked Stafford. Then he told of seeing Los Angeles, and Edwards Air Force Base and the runway. But finally the effort was too much. Sitting in the aft equipment bay and trying to don the portable maneuvering backpack, he became too tired. His breathing was heavy and in the deep cold of space, it was misting on his visor, icing like a window ices in winter. "My visor is all fogged up," Cernan said, weariness in his voice. He had been out now almost two hours. "He's fogging real bad," Stafford reported to earth. "It's far more difficult than in the simulations." "I can see where my nose is, but not where my eyeballs are," Cernan reported.

"Let's take a rest," Stafford told Cernan. Then to the ground he said, "It's about four or five times more work than we anticipated. And the pilot's visor is completely fogged over. Communications are very poor. He sounds like a loud gargle. If the situation doesn't improve . . . it's no go [on the backpack]."

Gemini Control concurred. Cernan, full of apologies, struggled back to the hatch. It took some time after he was sitting in his couch for his heartbeat to return to near normal level. He had been out on his space walk two hours and eight minutes, far more than any other human being. But it proved to flight designers that much more work had to be done on the ground before it would be practical for men to work and walk in space.

Like A Dog On A Leash— A Gemini spacecraft flies formation with its rendezvous target at the end of a 100-foot tether.

Gemini 9, working with its shipboard computer, produced the best landing in the Gemini series to that date, just one-half mile off target.

Gemini 9 had been a small step forward, and Gemini 10 took over from there. In July, Gemini 10 pilots John Young and Michael Collins headed into space with two rendezvous in its flight plan—one with a live bird, and one with a dead bird. The live bird was an Agena rocket launched specially for them. The dead bird was the Agena abandoned by Gemini 8 and still in orbit. In addition, Collins would have two 55-minute excursions outside the spacecraft. The pair also aimed at an altitude record using the rocket power of the Agena, if all worked well. And they would do all of this in three busy days. As Young put it, "Frankly, the mission has everything in it but the kitchen sink."

The Agena rocket was sent into orbit, and the Gemini 10 took off after it 100 minutes later. On the fourth revolution, Young and Collins zeroed in on the rocket and docked with it. It ate up some two-thirds of Gemini 10's maneuvering fuel. It should have only taken one-third of it. But now Gemini 10 had the Agena's jet and rocket power as well, so Gemini Control ordered a shutdown of the spacecraft's jets, and told the pilots to use the Agena's control system to handle the entire two-craft unit. Then, for the first time, Gemini 10 used the captive power of the Agena rocket to give their spacecraft a big boost in orbit—to a height of 476 miles, a new world record topping the Russian mark set by Leonov and Belyayev by more than 100 miles.

Collins made his first excursion in space, merely standing up in the open hatchway and photographing targets in the skies. But he had to cut this short because of eye irritation, eventually tracked down to lithium hydroxide in the spacesuit oxygen system. Lithium hydroxide is used to filter out carbon dioxide in used oxygen, and some had leaked into the system. "It smells sort of pungent in here," Young reported. "It really makes the eyes water."

He said he had noticed the problem earlier. "I was crying a little through the night, but I didn't say anything about it," he kidded. "I figured I'd be called a sissy."

The problem cleared up after Collins and Young returned to breathing the spacecraft's oxygen again. It didn't recur after that. Using the Agena's rocket power again, they chased down the Gemini 8 Agena that had been in orbit four months. Young described the feeling of driving the Gemini-Agena combination as being like "a railroad engineer driving down the road with a freight train, and all you can see is the freight train."

Now station-keeping or formation-flying with the dead Agena 8, Young jettisoned his own Agena and sent it flying to a safe distance away. "We have lost the Agena in the sunset," he told the ground. "It was a mighty good train."

Collins made his second excursion into space—this time flying up out of the hatch and over to the nearby Agena 8. Once there, he retrieved an experimental package from the side of the dead rocket, a package that measured the amount of tiny meteoric bits the Agena had encountered as it whipped around the earth. The package also contained a small microfilm note that said it had been retrieved by David Scott. Scott was unable to perform his space walk when Gemini 8 made its premature, emergency landing.

Collins was called back to Gemini 10 some 15 minutes early because the formation flying was using too much fuel. Back in the spaceship, he had to unhitch the 50-foot tether that had carried him oxygen in space, and throw it overboard with some dozen other pieces of excess equipment and debris.

The flight was a notable success. It enhanced experience in rendezvous and docking, and it helped pinpoint the problems in space walking—the difficulty of body positioning without anything to pull on or hold to. "We learned a great deal," said Dr. Robert Gilruth, director of the Manned Spacecraft Center.

But there was also another value to the flight, seldom mentioned. The military, without a manned space program of its own, was keenly interested in the Gemini spacecraft and the Gemini missions. It would later inherit the Gemini capability. But after Gemini 10, Air Force Gen. Leighton Davis, who headed military support for the flights, brought it up.

"This business of rendezvousing with an object in space is very important," he said. "The President has said that someday we must come to a full assurance that every object in space is there for peaceful purpose. The Air Force feels that we must have these capabilities to join with and rendezvous and inspect, if you will. And also we must have the capabilities to track and precisely determine what is going on and where things are up there."

It conjured up the Buck Rogers–Flash Gordon image of space patrols riding through the heavens to keep a world in peace. Wherever man goes, it seems, he brings his troubles and his doubts with him.

With two flights left to go in the Gemini program, the United States now had a wide lead over the Soviet Union. It had flown 14 manned flights to eight for the Russians. It had sent 22 men into space, twice as many as the Russians. It had compiled 1,661 hours and 52 minutes of man-hours in space, more than three times the total in the Soviet log. It had tallied two hours and 56 minutes of space walking to 10 minutes for the Soviet Union. And it had seven rendezvous and two dockings to none for the Soviet Union.

The moon looked bright indeed, and U.S. Surveyor craft had soft-landed there and beamed back to earth hundreds of pictures of the lunar surface, a beginning of a moon scan to find the best place to land.

There were all levels of consciousness about what was going on. But even for people involved in parts of the program, and for the American public with space-shots bursting into their collective privacy, there was seldom a realization of the whole effort. The money, the work, the ideas were bearing fruit, but a somehow un-spectacular fruit. Individuals might marvel at what man could do in any given in-stant, but there was rarely a notion of how far man had come, how far he had left to go, and why he should try at all.

On the planet, poverty, war, injustice. Above the planet, the test flights continued, expensive and somehow always the same. Forget the challenge of racing to the moon, some argued, forget the challenge of men seeking the limits of man's endeavor in space. With all of the troubles on earth, is this admittedly singular adventure worth the cost? Others argued, given a dollar, a man can always find excellent arguments for a dozen ways to spend it. Man, they said, has no greater cause than to probe the unknown.

No matter the arguments, in 1966 the space program reached a peak in spending—nearly $6 billion—and headed for a five-year decline. It reached a peak in employment—34,000 in-house workers and 360,000 contractor employees—and headed for a five-year decline. The peak of the moon effort had been reached, and there was nothing proposed to replace it as a major goal. The cost of the Vietnam war increased. The cost of domestic programs increased. The cost of the space program began to decrease in this year of 1966. Priorities vary in time, as do needs, on a practical scale.

In July of 1966, Rocco Petrone, who started with Von Braun working on the Redstone missile that eventually put Alan Shepard in space, became director of launch operations at Cape Kennedy. He was the man who remembered Sputnik with a sort of non-nationalistic scientific pride, who once marveled at how tall the 70-foot Redstone was. One day he would monitor the countdown for three men heading to the moon on top of a rocket more than 36 stories tall. He remembered Von Braun's dreams of space travel, of clustering small rockets into monster rockets. He was a University of Alabama graduate with German rocket experts for postgraduate tutors, and he wondered always why man shouldn't do what he thought he could do. To Petrone, mastering the countdowns in 1966, dollars and practical goals were not the measure of what he was doing.

"You look at Lindbergh's flight across the ocean," he said. "His flight cost him in the neighborhood of $15,000. And the prize, in monetary value, was $25,000. . . . Now a man has to be a fool to put his life on the line and lay down $15,000 to pick up $25,000. And that's the way people look at the space program. They say, 'I'm laying down $4 billion. What am I picking up?' . . . The idea of getting dollars for dollars, which is what the practical man says he's got to do, that isn't what made this country move."

Gemini was moving to a conclusion. In the space program, more than half of the difficulty was phrasing the questions to ask in unknown situations. The first 10 flights identified those questions fairly accurately. The next two flights would provide most of the answers with seemingly little effort. How difficult is working in space, in weightlessness, in an encumbering but necessary spacesuit? How difficult is rendezvous and docking? What will make it easier?

Project Mercury proved space flight was possible and tested some of the easy limits of man's ability in space. Project Gemini proved man could have a greater role than he dared dream of in flights at over 17,000 miles an hour, locked in the orbital law of circles, yet scooting around the heavens almost at will. Apollo and what came after would make use of both of them.

Gemini 11 was set for a September launch. The crew was Charles (Pete) Conrad,

New Route To The East—Gemini 11, circling the earth every hour-and-a-half, photographs India with Ceylon to the southeast.

who flew with Cooper on Gemini 5, and Navy Lt. Cmdr. Richard F. Gordon Jr., who had never flown before in space. To Gordon would fall a major chore, two world record stints of space walking between two spacecraft. Before the flight he read the dangers well: "There's nothing between you and oblivion except a pressure suit. You simply have to take your time, and you can't exhaust yourself."

Conrad and Gordon blasted off on September 12, barreling after an Agena target rocket and aiming for a rendezvous and docking in the first orbit, the quickest such a maneuver had been tried. The recorded heartbeats of both pilots more than doubled as the race began. With the radar searching the sky before them, the Gemini 11 pilots broke their busy silence to report, "Now we have visual sighting at 75 miles."

They closed in, nosed around and docked. Conrad reported in the technical term meaning they had linked up with the Agena. "Tell Mr. Kraft, would he believe M equals one?" Conrad said. "Roger," came the delighted reply from earth. "He believes you." "How about that?" Conrad kicked back.

It was more than an exercise in speed. It mimicked the maneuver astronauts leaving the moon in the space taxi would have to perform to join the mother ship on the first orbit. They repeated the docking maneuver and flew in formation with the Agena as well, ending up docked with the flying rocket for the night.

The next day was Gordon's. He stepped out into space for his first space walk, scheduled for 115 minutes, at the end of a 30-foot lifeline. But just trying to get the lifeline organized was too much. He began sweating profusely inside the spacesuit, and his breathing increased with effort. Finally, blinded by sweat, he was ordered back inside after 44 minutes. "Listen," Conrad told the earth, "I just brought Dick back in. He got so hot and sweaty he couldn't see." "I'm pooped," Gordon reported.

Getting his first real taste of the difficulty involved in moving under weightless conditions, Gordon sat astraddle the joined Gemini-Agena combine. "Ride it cowboy," Conrad said. He did one major chore, unstowing a 100-foot line and fixing one end of it to the Agena, so that they could undock the next day and see if a leash between two vehicles could save fuel and supplant formation flying. But first they used the Agena rocket to send them to a world record altitude of 850 miles, giving them a view of the earth no one had seen before. It was high enough to get a perspective of almost the whole earth, not just the curved quarter they were flying over.

"We're at the top of the world," Conrad called down. "I'll tell you, you can't believe it . . . utterly fantastic. The world is round . . . Just out my left window I can see all the way to the very end—all the way around about 150 degrees [nearly half a circle], with the horizon all the way around."

Later, Conrad stuck the upper half of his body out of the spacecraft and spent more than two hours taking pictures of stars and other prescribed targets in space. Over Texas, he looked down and told Gemini Control, "It looks beautiful down there. Gorgeous." Acting as capsule communicator, John Young beamed back kiddingly, "See those kids on the roof?" Gordon, whose children have a reputation for roof-climbing, said, "They'd better not be there."

Without Boundaries— Men make borders. The earth has few of its own. This is a picture of the Middle East, torn by recurrent crisis and war, taken from 175 miles up by Gemini 11. From Egypt, across the Gulf of Suez, the Sinai, Israel, Jordan, Syria, the camera captured an area of about 750,000 miles.

One of their last experiments was to pull away from the Agena, keeping the rocket on the end of the 100-foot leash. "This is really weird," Conrad reported. "It's like the Agena and I have got a skip rope between us. It's rotating and making a big loop. I've got things pretty well in hand now, and it looks like we're skipping rope with the thing out there." As he kept pulling the tether taut, it gradually cut down the bowing in the line.

Finally, he reported, "This thing has stabilized completely. It's [the Agena] sticking straight out from our nose on the end of the tether. We're looking right down our nose at it. We're nice and steady and stable . . . We wouldn't have believed it two hours ago."

Then, using an explosive disconnect device, they dropped the leash from the Gemini's nose, leaving the Agena and the tether behind. "The tether slowly wrapped itself around the Agena like a Christmas present," Conrad reported excitedly. "You're so dramatic," chided Gemini Control. The next day they landed within two miles of the recovery ship with some of the most vivid pictures taken from space.

The problem of space walking and working was still not solved. Gordon had not been able to try out the tools and handrails provided experimentally on Gemini 11. The 21-layer spacesuit was too restraining. Gordon's exertion was so great he put three times the heat load into the suit than it was meant to handle. The 30-second job of tying the tether to the Agena had taken 30 minutes. He even had trouble sitting astraddle the spacecraft and rocket. "I kept floating off," he said.

"We have to keep the tasks simple," Gordon said, "so that they can be done with one hand until we develop some sort of restraints . . . If you can provide proper restraints so he can use both hands, I think the nuts and bolts operations will come by naturally. Eventually we will be able to do that."

One mystery of the flight was solved later. At one point, Conrad found another flying object. "We have a wingman flying wing on us here, off to my left, tumbling about one revolution a second," he reported from space. The North American Defense Command checked. "The wingman" was Russia's Proton 3 satellite, launched a year before, a 27,000-pound monster, largest ever orbited. The two space programs, strangers on earth, met in the skies.

Gemini 12, last of the sons of Mercury, last of the fathers of Apollo. Born on November 11, 1966, it was piloted by two blond, blue-eyed Americans, one a West Pointer, one a Naval Academy graduate, both destined to have an intimate, a personal, knowledge of the moon.

James Lovell's nickname was Shakey, because of his sociability, not out of any undue nervousness. Edwin E. Aldrin's nickname was Buzz, so named by his parents. Both were experienced in jet aircraft, and standard aircraft. Lovell was a veteran of the marathon Gemini 7 flight, and with the blastoff of Gemini 12 would have more time in space than any other American astronaut. Aldrin was a rookie. Lovell was an experienced test pilot. Aldrin was a Korean veteran with two MIGs to his credit. Third in his class at West Point, Aldrin earned a doctorate in astronautics at the Massachusetts Institute of Technology in 1963, long before many schools offered such a degree. His thesis was on space rendezvous before it was ever tried.

A few hours after blastoff, they caught a target Agena rocket after a 64,000-mile chase. Then they docked with it. They had to cancel a plan to use the Agena for boost into a higher orbit because of rocket trouble. But they were able to use a smaller rocket on the Agena to supplement their own control system.

They chased the moon across South America and photographed it eclipsing the sun. But they couldn't find the moon's shadow as it cut a 50-mile wide shadow across the continent. Then, for three successive days, Buzz Aldrin followed a program of space stands and space walks, using new restraint belts, handrails and tools that proved once and for all that man could work in space. The first day he merely poked his head and shoulders out of the spacecraft hatch and snapped unforgettable pictures of the stars and earth. His heart rate and respiration were nearly normal. "What did I tell you, Buzz," Lovell told him, "four days vacation with pay and see the world."

The first outing lasted two hours and 15 minutes. Aldrin took listeners on a travel tour of earth. "Tell everybody to smile down there," he said as he aimed his camera at Texas. "There's the Cape [Kennedy]," he said over Florida. "I'd like to go skin-diving down there . . . Looks like a few clouds over the Cape." As he changed position to get a better angle, Lovell cautioned him, "Watch it. Watch it. Get your foot out of the way. You've got it on the switch for the fuel cells." In Gemini Control, Marilyn Lovell and Joan Aldrin, their wives, sat in visitor's chairs and listened to the dialogue for some 90 minutes.

The second outing was a complete one. It lasted two hours and nine minutes, by one minute the longest space walk to date. Calm and taking frequent rest periods, Aldrin used handrails on the spaceship, and floated free at the end of a 30-foot lifeline. It went so well that he stayed out 13 minutes longer than planned. During one rest break he launched his own satellite, a small white nylon pennant, commemorating Veterans Day, the day Gemini 12 was launched. "I have an emblem here I'd like to leave in orbit," he said. "I'd like to extend the meaning to include all the people of the world who stand for now and continue to strive for peace and freedom in the world."

"Mighty fine," acknowledged Gemini Control. "Wait," said Aldrin. "I've got another one here. This message concerns a contest coming up in the future." With that he released another pennant, that West Pointer Aldrin said was inscribed, "Go Army, Beat Navy."

"Ah, Roger, understand," said Naval Academy graduate William Anders in Gemini Control, capsule communicator who chose to misunderstand. "Beat Army," he said.

"I knew we had the wrong cap com," said Aldrin. He then asked his space companion, Lovell, also a Naval Academy graduate, to photograph him in space holding the pennant. "What a terrible job," Lovell said. "I hate to do it."

The third outing was another stand-up exercise, and Aldrin photographed the sunrise and the Milky Way. This stint lasted some 52 minutes. In all, he was exposed to the hostility of space for some 5½ hours over the three days, and dispelled once

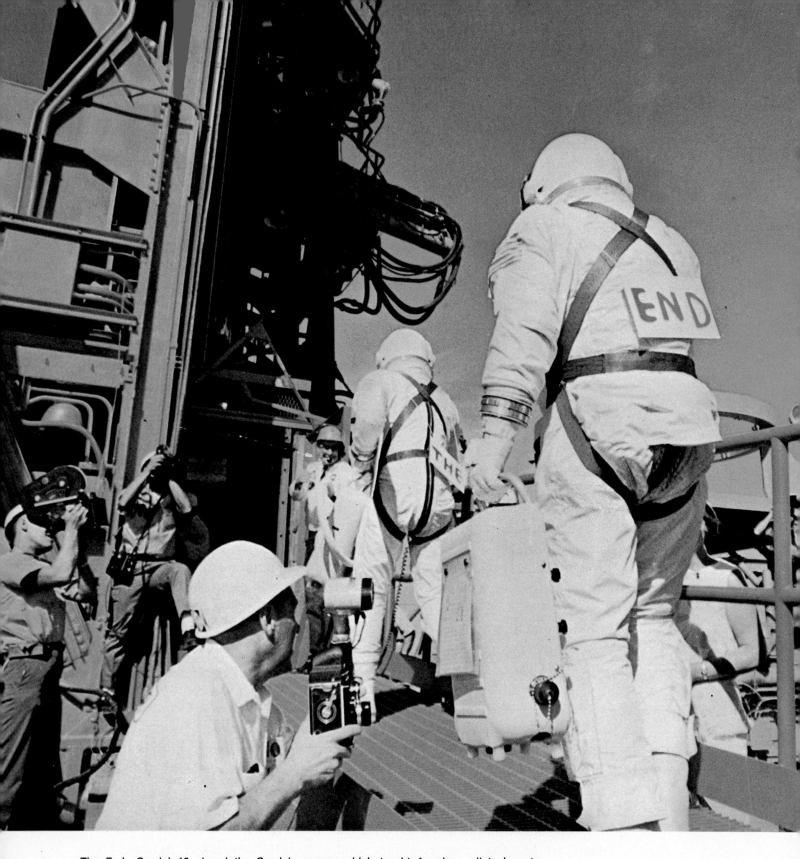

The End—Gemini 12 closed the Gemini program which taught American pilots how to rendezvous and dock in space, how to work in a weightless state. It proved that man needs something to hang onto, some point of leverage, in a world where every action has its direct and opposite reaction. Here the Gemini 12 pilots, Lovell and Aldrin, in that order, mount the gantry for their near earth adventure. Both would one day see the moon close-up.

Champion Spacewalker—Edwin (Buzz) Aldrin took all spacewalking records on the Gemini 12 flight, gathered some excellent pictures of earth, and learned to walk on the moon.

Ride It Cowboy—Richard Gordon rides astraddle the docked Gemini 11 and its Agena. He hooked up a 100-foot line so the two craft could separate and yet remain together without unnecessary use of fuel.

and for all any question of man's ability to walk and work on the moon in a heavy spacesuit.

The maneuvering jets on Gemini 12 were going out one by one, and to insure the ability to control the spaceship on re-entry, the last day was spent in lazy, drifting flight. "To save fuel, we're just going to let it drift," Lovell told Gemini Control. "We're doing it now."

That night, Gemini Control beamed popular music up to the astronauts. At first they had some trouble getting through. "Did you get the music?" Control asked. "Not yet," Lovell replied. "What are they playing?"

"Going back to Houston," said Gemini Control. "What else?"

The next day the spacecraft splashed down in the Atlantic within sight of the recovery carrier *USS Wasp*, the last stanza in the Gemini program that worked out the methods and the means to land Americans on the moon. In Gemini Control they broke out cigars, and at a news conference, they broke out wine and toasted the program. Said spacecraft center director Dr. Gilruth, "Gemini has given us a great legacy to the space program. With today's flight we've completed 10 manned flights and have done all the things that we had to do as a prelude to Apollo."

Said President Johnson, "We know America is in space to stay." But the President also cautioned, prophetically, "The months ahead will not be easy as we reach for the moon."

Space agency chief James Webb, aware of problems in design of the three-man Apollo spacecraft, tempered the optimism, too. "Perhaps, as the President did, I should add a word of caution," he said. "We are currently operating on a success schedule. Things have been going extremely well. However, we are already beginning to encounter development problems that will cause delays in Apollo. There has been some slippage in our success plan."

The first flight of the Apollo spacecraft and a three-man crew was now tentatively planned for January, 1967, a slip of two months. The crew had been named in March. Command pilot was to be Virgil I. (Gus) Grissom, veteran of early Mercury and Gemini test flights, now set to test the spaceship that would go to the moon. His crew included the first American space walker, Ed White, and a rookie, Navy Lt. Roger B. Chaffee.

The year 1966 ended with glowing pride in America's new found space prowess. The year 1967 would begin with bitter blows, unforeseen and tragic events for both the United States and the Soviet Union, that would make the moon seem distant again.

# 9 'Fire In The Spacecraft'

There was little to be happy about with Apollo. Gus Grissom, who would be its first command pilot, knew it.

The pressure was on. The space agency was pressing for Apollo's first flight in November, 1966, but trouble piled on trouble and the date slipped to December, then January, 1967. Behind it all was another lingering question, what were the Russians doing?

Grissom and his crew, Ed White and Roger Chaffee, trying to sharpen flying procedures, felt that the spacecraft trainer at Cape Kennedy wasn't good enough. One morning, disgusted, Grissom hung a lemon on it. When he talked privately, he was open in his pessimism. He just didn't think the Apollo had the stamina to last the full two weeks set for the mission.

"We've been hard-pressed for trainers and training time," he said at one point. "If we had to fly the first of December, I think we would have been hard-pressed to get ourselves ready."

What created the pressure? Was it the success of Gemini? Or the Russian unknown? Everything seemed to conspire against Apollo. Low public interest, a cost-conscious Congress, and a balky, expensive spacecraft and rocket, each so complex it was difficult to measure its potential safety. In December, 1966, Joseph F. Shea, the spacecraft manager, cited "something like 20,000" test failures. "We hope to God there is no safety involved in the things that slip through," he said.

The Apollo 1 spacecraft was accepted by the agency in August, 1966. It took North American Aviation Corp. two years to build. There were continual design changes, and then, in the space agency's hands, more troubles—the radio system, power system, oxygen and water supply, cooling. The shot date slipped again to February 26, 1967. Grissom, a veteran of two test flights in Mercury and Gemini, normally quiet, easy-going, a flight pro, could not hide his irritation. "Pretty slim" was the way he put his Apollo's chances of meeting its mission requirements.

Project Apollo was one of the most complex scientific and engineering programs man had ever devised. At one point or another, 300,000 people and 20,000 companies were involved. The spacecraft alone had two million working parts. Earlier space-craft, Gemini and Mercury, were relatively simple. Each part of their design could be followed by the personal interest of one man, or one group of men, beginning to end. Not so Apollo. It was so complex, it was designed system by system, each integrated into the whole. It was also the first designed and built by North American. Gemini and Mercury were products of McDonnell Aircraft Corp. The change in contractors meant training new people, and the loss of the experience and team spirit of the old, although this alone could not explain Apollo's difficulties. Perhaps they were best explained by the complexity and size.

Shea was open about the spaceship's troubles in December as time dwindled for Grissom, White and Chaffee. Continued testing found more weaknesses. But just how perfect did everything have to be? There were two kinds of problems, Shea said —those that had to be fixed, and those just shy of design specifications. In the last category, how many do you accept? How many do you send back? Shea described the space agency's policy as: "Run the program in a balanced way, don't try to make everything too perfect, don't try to make anything too complex, or you'll never get the job done."

Human error was naggingly present in two early unmanned Apollo flights. Shea explained, "That combination of problems, none of which is major, still made us feel pretty nervous about the over-all system operation. We obviously fixed those prob-lems, but the question that you're always left with is, how many are going to creep through the next time?"

There was also trouble with the developing Saturn 5 rocket, the one that would finally blast off to the moon with the power of 543 jet-fighters. A second stage engine exploded during a test because someone failed to connect some switches. "Personal goofs," said a space agency official. A third stage engine exploded because some weld-ing filler was short of specifications.

Nevertheless, Grissom's Apollo 1 was moved to Launch Complex 34 on January 6, still aiming for the late February blastoff. It was hoisted to the top of the Saturn 1 rocket, an already proven forerunner of the bigger Saturn 5. There was even trouble on the launch pad. Testing ran behind schedule. To save time, the space agency took a shortcut. It skipped a preliminary test that would have overfilled the spacecraft with its 100 per cent oxygen atmosphere before the astronauts entered the test pro-cedure.

On the morning of January 27, 1967, Grissom, White and Chaffee were suited up and ready to enter the spacecraft for what was called a "plugs out" test, to check the compatibility of all systems in a countdown rehearsal. It was the first time the cabin was pressurized with 100 per cent oxygen when the astronauts finally entered at 1:19 p.m. after minor delays.

Immediately, the pilots complained of a sour smell in the cabin. "The Watermelon Gang," air testers who use a watermelon-like tank, were called for, but the odor dis-appeared before they arrived. An hour later, the smell returned, and the air testers

The One That Worked—Could the Saturn 5 prove itself? When it did, in the unmanned flight of Saturn 501, it was a dazzling success that gave the men of the moon program new heart.

"Ignition . . . Liftoff"—Saturn-Apollo 6, unmanned again, proves out the entire system, despite some minor engine problems. These pictures, taken by an automated camera in the gantry, catch the power of Saturn 5 rising from the earth trailing an 800-foot tail of flame.

were called in again. They found nothing unusual in the air sample. But the space-craft was having other troubles. Grissom complained again and again of bad com-munications with controllers. "If I can't talk to you five miles away," he said, "how can we talk to you on the moon?" After repeated holds to check the communications, the countdown wore down to its final 10 minutes. At this point, someone suggested post-poning the test. But officials decided that time was too precious. It was overruled.

The countdown was holding now for a communications check. The men had been in the spacecraft more than five hours. The countdown was to begin again at 6:31 p.m. It never did.

Perhaps a minute before, instruments in the ship showed a rise in oxygen flow in the spacesuit systems. It indicated movement by one of the astronauts, maybe Gris-som. There were also unclear shouts. Four seconds later, Chaffee's voice jarred through everyone's consciousness: "We've got a fire in the spacecraft."

In the choking course of events, the astronauts began emergency procedures, White reaching over his left shoulder to set up the release of the inner hatch. Grissom was to pull a handle to depressurize the cabin. Perhaps he could not, certainly he did not do it. Officials were not sure whether he couldn't reach it because of the rushing flames, or whether he had already succumbed to the fire, or whether he forgot in the rush of events.

But without the release of the cabin pressure, the inner hatch would not open, held there by the strong press of the spacecraft atmosphere. As it turned out in the next few seconds, it didn't matter. The three astronauts were doomed.

From inside the spacecraft, their voices tumbled over one another, reports of "a bad fire . . . we're burning up . . . open her up . . . I'm getting out." No one is sure of the words or voices. There was a cry of pain. In seconds, the spacecraft inner hull ruptured on the floor to the right of Chaffee. With this sudden vent, the fire, which started below Grissom on the left, swept across White in the middle and Chaffee, sucked toward its new escape route between the two hulls, then engulfed the spacecraft itself. The astronauts died in the first 18 seconds, their death certificates showing death by asphyxiation, specifically carbon monoxide inhalation. Mercifully, they did not feel most of the pain of the fire. They were unconscious before they died.

Twenty-seven men working on various levels around the rocket dashed to the spacecraft hatch. They worked futilely, fuel-proof masks failing to protect them against the poisonous smoke. It took them five minutes, working in relays in the smoke and heat, to open the hatch. A minute-and-a-half later, a doctor arrived to find there was nothing he could do for the astronauts. But all 27 workmen required medi-cal treatment.

In Apollo Control's Launch Operations Room, two of the big, mural-sized television screens were focused on the awful scene. Rocco Petrone, director of launch opera-tions, will never forget the helplessness. The picture is burned into his mind. "When that cry came out—'Fire in the spacecraft'—I looked at the TV screen. I saw some-thing going on, I saw a shake, I thought I saw a flash inside the ship. It was just utter helplessness. Just nothing you could do. You couldn't get to them . . . The thing exploded in 19 seconds . . . fire shot out the side . . . I didn't see the fire but I saw the thing shake cables, and I knew it was downstairs in the service module . . . Those minutes, needless to say, were heart-rending . . . They did finally get it open . . . It was an eternity. Then I recall how the spacecraft crew searched inside and I asked them, 'Can you do something for the guys?' They said, 'No, it's too late' . . . The only thing I could do was shut off the television, so we wouldn't be looking."

In the months after, Petrone remembered, "You kept asking yourself, could you have done more? Was there something you didn't do? Was there something your team didn't do? That was what you kept searching yourself for." Through the inquiry, there was criticism that the space agency was not the proper unit to be doing the investigating. Petrone felt it was unfounded: "We didn't want to whitewash it. What the hell do we want to whitewash? We're scientists. We're engineers. We're not politicians. We're not running for office. We want to get this thing on the road. And in order to do it, you've got to find out what was wrong. You don't go into a laboratory and make a mistake and cover up . . . Many people can't understand that in the outside world. I guess maybe they're used to other things. We had to investigate ourselves. There was just no one else who could do it. The thing was so complex, so complicated. The language alone. We brought in some people from the outside, one of them an expert on mine explosions and fires. It took him literally weeks to understand the language. Throughout, we had to keep asking ourselves, was there something more we could have done to save these guys? Was there something we should have seen?"

Even normally, probably no agency is as introspective as the space agency. It is constantly looking back, analyzing procedures, systems, specifications, equipment. It provides overseers for itself and its contractors, prying into its operations, looking for weaknesses. It now created an investigating board to look into the causes of the fire.

In the next self-critical months, more than 1,500 experts pored over the sooted remains of the Apollo 1 spaceship. The fire was re-enacted in another spacecraft. After 10 weeks, the board produced its report, a masterpiece of introspection. It found both the space agency and North American guilty of poor management, carelessness, negligence, design deficiencies, and a failure to consider the safety of the astronauts adequately. The board decided the likely cause of the fire was faulty wiring, and an exposed arc of electricity that ignited materials in the spacecraft. An ally to the fire was the pure oxygen environment, since burning is, after all, a combining of other elements with oxygen. There was plenty of oxygen available. The oxygen pressure in the spacecraft was more than three times as high as it would be in space, the aim being to prevent any earthly contaminants from flowing into the cabin.

Officials sadly admitted that they had failed to recognize the fire hazard in this one procedure. In space, the fire could have been snuffed out by venting the oxygen, reducing the cabin environment to a vacuum. Not so on earth.

The board ordered major changes in design: sheathing with metal all wiring

previously exposed, replacement of virtually all flammable materials in the cabin with flame-resistant materials, better communications, better armor on joints to prevent leakage, new nonflammable spacesuits and, importantly, a gas operated hatch that could be opened in less than seven seconds compared to the Apollo 1 double hatch that took 90 seconds to open under normal conditions.

There were dozens of other changes in fire-proofing and failure-proofing, and a lot more work to be done before Apollo would fly.

The effect on the thousands in the program was beyond measure. Despair lingered over Cape Kennedy and Houston for months. It haunts the men there still. No one was in a self-forgiving mood, no one would find solace in what Gus Grissom once said, "If we die, we want people to accept it. We are in a risky business and we hope that if anything happens to us, it will not delay the program. The conquest of space is worth the risk of life."

The space race had plunged from the brilliant success of Gemini to the awful despair of Apollo 1 in just three months. In the long run, the lessons of the fire would enhance the coming models of the three-man spaceships just as surely it would delay them. Said one close to the scene: "The Apollo program is like the street corner that doesn't get a traffic light until somebody is killed there by a car."

If the carelessness had been born of the need to race the Russians, there was irony here too. Three months after the fire, on April 23, 1967, the Soviet Union launched its first model of a big new spacecraft called Soyuz I, with Col. Vladimir Komarov at the controls. He was 40, a father, and a veteran of the Soviet air force from the age of 15. His flight went off without prior notice, in the Russian custom. Indeed, his wife didn't know he was in space until a fellow pilot called her 25 minutes after the launch.

The meaning of the Soviet flight was full of portent. Soyuz meant union. The aim obviously was to rendezvous and dock with another spacecraft. The idea was obviously to match or surpass what had been accomplished by Gemini in techniques to reach the moon. The flight bulletins reported Komarov well, and orbit normal. Komarov broadcast his greetings to the Soviet nation and saluted "the courageous Vietnamese people fighting against the bandit aggression of American imperialism."

Then, after about 27 hours, the flight bulletins ceased. For 11 hours there was silence, then a terse announcement. The parachutes failed on descent to earth. Komarov was killed in the crash landing. He was the first human to be lost in space flight.

Not everyone believed that the tragedy could be so easily explained. Some U.S. officials wondered if something might have gone wrong with the spacecraft well before its scheduled landing. Was it tumbling, or out of control? Was it forced to land? And with its control system in trouble, did it then crash? Some sources in the Soviet Union later suggested that the mission of Soyuz I included rendezvous and docking with a second ship in a spectacular transfer of crews. No one knew for sure. But Vladimir Komarov was dead after a space flight of 18 orbits: 26 hours and 48 minutes. One more element appeared to be certain, as the first man in space, Yuri Gagarin, said a month later: "The flight of a new ship of the Soyuz type will be possible only when

Across The Night Sky—Saturn 5 cuts an arc with its blazing exhaust as it programs out over the Atlantic from Cape Kennedy's launch complex.

Bound For Orbit—A Saturn 5 streaks across the azure sky for the darkness of space. Sixty feet taller than the Statue of Liberty and, with a full load of fuel, 13 times as heavy.

all circumstances of the accident of the first ship are completely investigated, the causes removed and new tests carried out. All of this naturally takes time."

The dynamics of human endeavor are not so different between nations. The dispirit that descended on the American space team descended on the Russian. If the American accident armed American opponents of space flight, the Russian accident likely armed the Russian counterparts. At any rate, it would be 16 months before another man would fly a Soyuz spaceship.

There was one other similarity between the two tragedies. Months after U.S. astronauts saluted their fallen friends, Yuri Gagarin stood at Komarov's funeral and said, "We shall always remember you, our dear Volodya [affectionate for Vladimir], and we shall worthily continue the cause for which you have sacrificed your bright and beautiful life." The Soviet cosmonaut who embraced American space fliers in Athens, who shared with them the thrill of flying, shared also the pride and the grief that is the camaraderie of adventurers.

Both space programs now were under deep questioning, each in its own country. In the United States, those who felt that manned space flight was an unnecessary, unscientific extravagance chose this moment to argue their point. There was even criticism along political lines. Space agency chief James Webb found it "a convergence of a great many people who said, 'Now is the time to let them have it.'"

"Staging"—Automatic cameras catch the moment when the main rocket of Saturn 5 separates from the rest of the rocketry, its job done, and fresh rocket engines take over.

Years later, still stung by criticisms that he felt were unjust, he said they "made us look like we were a bunch of bums who didn't know what we were doing. Now that was a very grave disappointment and a very real, heart-rending experience for a great many people in NASA, including me. I was surprised that a good deal of what was being done was out in front of our own system. And that the checks and balances of our own internal system were not being applied by our own people."

But in those months following the fire, Webb said, "There was only one thing to do, and that was to pitch in and fix the problems, and make them fly—which we did. There clearly was no one who could make an investigation of why things burn in spacecraft any better than we could. The question was not who was at fault. The question was how do you find out why this thing really burned, and fix it so that the next one doesn't burn? That was the real question. And the public never seemed to understand that. They were looking for some way of fixing blame.

"Some of the people," Webb said, "were calling for a congressional investigating commission. Some of the people around the White House were worried about how this would affect the President. I just went to him and said, 'I'm prepared to do the job. I think I can do it as well as anybody you can get. If you want a commission, that's just fine with me. You can have whatever you want. I just expect one thing. If I'm going to do it, then I want to know that I'm going to have the chance to do it, until you decide you want to take it out of my hands. And if you're going to take it out of my hands, I want you to tell me first.'

"That's the only time I ever struck a bargain with the President. He stuck out his hand and we shook hands, and that was a deal. I went right on about it."

Chaffee, White And Grissom—In that order from left to right. The fire started below Grissom's couch, spread across the cabin toward a hole the heat had blown in the spacecraft's inner hull. Mercifully, they died in 18 seconds. Their memory would remain with the space program all the way to the moon.

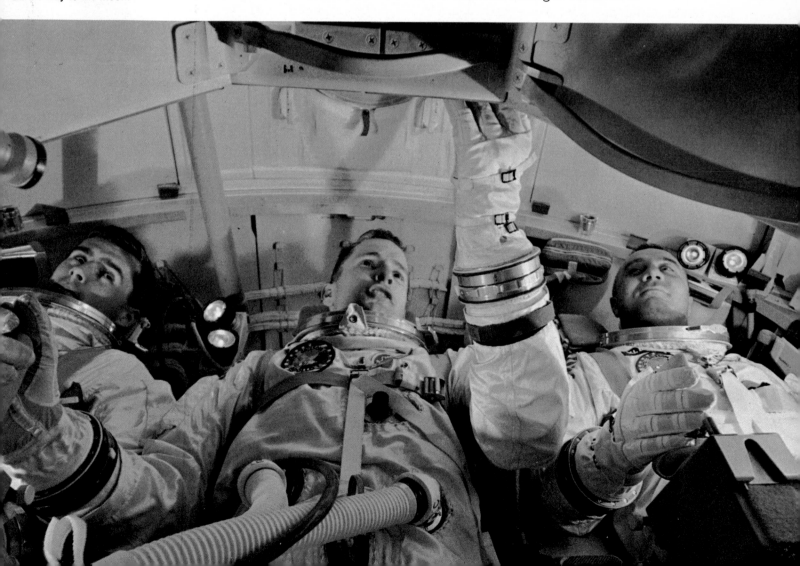

Through The Hatch—A view of the gutted remains of the Apollo's complicated wiring after the fire.

Indeed, despite the despair, the space agency went right on about it. There was not so much a new spirit as a new conception of purpose, the same sense of urgency, a chastened confidence. They were ready again in November, dedicated now to a more cautious course, the repairs made and the procedures set up for the Apollo spacecraft and the mighty, new Saturn 5 rocket, monstrous in every detail—92 engines and 15 miles of wiring, 36 stories tall, full of potential glory or potential destruction, laden with so much fuel that, if it blew up, its flames would reach out in a 3,000-foot diameter.

On November 9, 1967, it stood on the launch pad that would one day be the pedestal to reach the moon. This was an unmanned flight tabbed Apollo 4 to most people. But it was Saturn 501 to the men who would launch it. It was an all-out test, everything, all three rocket stages, the Apollo spacecraft, and a moon-style re-entry, a third again as fast and hotter than re-entry from earth orbit. It had everything but men. Considering, the space experts would settle for a partial success, although no one would admit it. Certainly it was doubtful that everything would work. That would be almost too much to hope.

Too much to hope? The man who guided the launch, Rocco Petrone, remembers: "I feel that 501, working the way it did, spacecraft and all, kind of got us back in the right swing, where the American public and the Congress could say, 'Yeah, those guys can do it.'

"There was a hell of a lot riding on 501. More than just that launch. Proving of the whole concept, proving we knew what we were doing—first time out with the most complex launch vehicle man had ever dreamed of—brand new . . . It went a long way toward getting us back on the road . . . What we're saying is, 501 was the result of seven years of effort. Seven years of drive. It's there, no question. As an accomplishment, it's very high on my mind."

So it went that November day. If they cried, "Go straight, go true, John Glenn, go, go, go," they cried it for this rocket and spacecraft without a man in it. And it flew.

For eight or nine seconds after ignition, with flame roaring out of its mammoth tail, and the thousands of gallons of water trying to tame the heat before it melted the

Postmortem—Experts pored over the remains of the Apollo fire to find out how to prevent such accidents in the future. Said one, "The Apollo program is like the street corner that doesn't get a traffic light until somebody is killed there by a car."

structure of the launching pad, it sat there. Then, released by the clamps that held it to earth, it rose. Lumbering. Horrible in its noise. A spectacle which the eyes could not believe and the ears could not stand. At the press site, the corrugated metal roof literally bounced to the pulse of the engines. Temporary quarters, built without the knowledge of Saturn 5, tumbled down. It was one wild moment, the engines gulping 15 tons of fuel a second and belching out an 800-foot flame, struggling against the very thing that holds man to his easy chair, gravity. It roared and it screamed and there were no gentle terms to its voice. It moved. And it couldn't be true. The first stage drilled the mammoth complex into the sky and, its work done, dropped away, with the second stage rocket—like the second man in a relay team—starting fresh with the baton, faster, faster, faster. Then the third stage, and it was in orbit with a power man had never seen before except for destruction.

Quiet now, it whirled in mathematical synchrony with the other elements of space. There was no man in it, but one day there would be.

Now the 278,700-pound monster rode through the heavens, then kicked itself into a false-start to the moon, turned around and dashed back to earth. Born in the heat of the launch eight-and-a-half hours before, it blasted back into the earth's atmosphere, the gases around its frame reaching over 5,000 degrees, mimicking a return to earth from the moon. Everything did work, precisely, the countdown, the launch exactly on time, the engines, the whole complex inorganic organism, not human, but almost, it all worked. In less than a year, the United States space program had picked up its dirty laundry and cleansed itself, and was back on the schedule it had set for itself, the moon before 1970.

To add to the dazzle of 501, the Surveyor spacecraft—also without men—were charting the lunar surface, close up. Since Surveyor 1 had landed on the moon and transmitted over 11,000 pictures in 1966, other Surveyors had pressed their feet into the lunar surface, analyzed the soil, found mammoth craters and tiny craters, the result of an ageless bombardment from space. They found rocks, and dirt tumbling down slopes and catching on rocks, and a filmy, dusty soil, brighter in some places, darker in others, but nearly the same in the light it reflected, gray apparently, in a world where color is meaningless. The most common elements on the surface, remarkably like earth, are oxygen, silicon and aluminum and, below that, basaltic material with a varying iron content. The program cost $560 million, and with Surveyor 7 in January 1968 it brought home almost 90,000 close-in pictures of the lunar surface at five different sites, highland and headland, crater bottom and valley. It dug, sensed and questioned the soil that would one day feel the foot of man. In addition, Surveyor 6 used a rocket to blast off from the moon, as man would one day, on his way home.

Also in January 1968, the United States launched Apollo 5, an unmanned spacecraft atop a Saturn 1 rocket. It carried a prototype of the lunar module in its first successful test. In April following, the United States launched an unmanned Apollo 6 aboard a Saturn 5 rocket, and discovered a number of engine problems, none of them unsolvable. The pace was picking up.

The Russians, meanwhile, were doing bewildering things. Twice, in 1967 and in 1968, they launched Cosmos satellites, unmanned, and guided them to automatic rendezvous and docking, both remarkable maneuvers without the eyes and hands of humans to guide them in the skies.

On October 1, 1968, the space agency celebrated its 10th anniversary, counted its successes and failures, and got ready to launch Apollo 7 on the 11th. It noted that in its first 10 years, it had launched 234 spacecraft, counted 191 flight successes, 176 fully successful missions. It also noted that Apollo 4, the successful Saturn 501, weighed more than all of the other U.S. spacecraft combined.

Now there was a broadening base of confidence in Apollo. Some skepticism persisted to insure its success. Wally Schirra, another old veteran of Mercury and Gemini flights, took over as command pilot for the new Apollo 7. Several months before, he had said, "I'll buy it when I know it will fly all the way." Now he was saying, "We have attained the confidence that we need to fly a manned space flight again, and I'm ready to fly it."

Much had been done to Apollo. The North American people tightened up on every procedure. The head of a socket wrench that had been found in the Apollo 1 cabin after the fire became a symbol of sloppiness and a grim reminder of the need for care. A special list limited the number of people allowed to enter the spacecraft. A guard at the hatch checked every nut, bolt and tool that went inside. TV cameras kept constant watch on all spacecraft activities. Women working on the ship had to scrub off all cosmetics, and either remove or put tape over their rings. Men had to shower to re-

They Called It Wally's Ship—The space veteran Schirra (center, sitting) took an extra interest in the development of Apollo 7, the first manned attempt after the fire. He was its captain. Here he studies an orbital map with fellow crewmen Donn Eisele and Walter Cunningham (sitting left to right) and astronaut coordinator Deke Slayton (standing).

move loose hair after haircuts. It became known as "Wally's ship" to all of the red-badged people who worked on it.

At 45, Wally Schirra would be the oldest man to fly into space, his 18-year-old son almost old enough to be an astronaut himself. A 90-mission veteran of the Korean war, Schirra was a veteran Navy test pilot before his nine-hour flight in Mercury 7 and his premiere rendezvous flight with Tom Stafford in Gemini 6. Both of his space flights were catalogued "textbook" quality in their perfection.

One official admitted, "I'll feel a lot better with Wally flying this one." But for all of his hard-headed flying ability, Schirra was also taking a hard look at himself and when he should quit. Before the flight, he said: "I think when I find I'm just too plain tired, when I can't keep up the pace, this very rapid pace, then I would personally consider it . . . There is some point in your life, and a man can judge fairly well, if he's honest with himself. And this is much too important a business for me to just have personal pride and keep on going until I might stumble. I'll have to learn when to hang up my spurs."

In the days following, he decided. The flight of Apollo 7 would be his last.

Schirra's crewmates were Walter Cunningham, 36, a former Marine flier who

Colds In Space—The Apollo 7 crew worked so hard preparing that they caught colds that developed after they were in space. In the new, complex system, the men were hard-pressed to keep up with the machines.

needed only his thesis to win his doctorate in physics at the University of California, and Donn P. Eisele, 38, a Naval Academy graduate who switched to the Air Force, who lost both his parents within five days in 1964, and who fought a shoulder injury to keep his flight status.

As the men geared up for their flight, there were other space developments. The Senate ratified a United Nations-approved treaty providing for the rescue and return of astronauts downed on foreign soil by flight accident or emergency. Russia had already ratified the pact, as had 74 other nations. And at Cape Kennedy, Dr. Wernher von Braun warned that the Soviet Union could be on the verge of launching a big, new rocket that would enhance their chances of getting to the moon. But most U.S. experts doubted Von Braun's prognostication.

The talk could have been a symptom of frustration among space agency experts. Beginning the flights that would eventually reach the moon, they sensed a new low in public interest and congressional support. There was something distressing about the attitude of the man on the street. He had begun to look at space flight as a stunt sometime before, and he would not get the idea out of his mind. Space flight proponents took every occasion to emphasize the race with the Russians, and some were beginning to distrust this. For one thing, it began to look as if the Russians weren't in the race. Now others were trying to sell the idea of other benefits from space flight, miniature electronic devices, non-stick frying pans, international television, better weather reports, materials that would be useful in other industries, anything that could be made to seem as if it came from the space program. But no argument seemed to stick in the public mind, and the dedicated men who believed in space exploration were bewildered.

President Johnson had tried to put it understandably. He said, "If we got nothing else from the space program than the photographic satellite, it is worth 10 times over the money we've spent. Without the satellites, I'd be operating by guess and by God. But I know exactly how many missiles the enemy has got." It pointed up one little known fact. Of some 450 satellites launched by the United States at that time, 340 had military assignments. The same was true of the Soviet Union. It had launched some 224 satellites, nearly half of them for military purposes. The feedback from military satellite programs would in later years spawn a need for anti-ballistic missile systems to counter Red China, and a growing debate on the defensive posture of the United States.

But in 1968, the U.S. moon program was facing a much more shadowy enemy—public apathy—and no one knew what to do about it.

Schirra, Cunningham and Eisele shot into space on October 11, on an intended 11-day trip around the earth to test the stamina of the Apollo spacecraft. From the beginning, the spacecraft behaved beautifully. Moving around in the large cabin, the astronauts had more freedom than in any previous flight. They also had such heretofore unavailable luxuries as hot and cold running water.

But on the second day, the first signs of trouble began to appear, not with the spacecraft, but with the crew. The flight plan was jammed with events, like rendez-vousing with a spent rocket engine, and using the spacecraft's engine to maneuver. Schirra, plagued with a sudden cold, took a hard-nosed attitude to Mission Control's desire to have them televise events inside the spacecraft.

"We have a new vehicle up here," he said. "I'm saying at this point, television will be delayed, without any further discussion, until after the rendezvous." The ground argued, pleaded, "All we're agreed to do on this particular pass is to flip the television switch on. No other activity is associated with TV. I think we're still obligated to do that." Schirra's voice, husky with the cold, turned hard, and he spoke in rapid, clipped tones: "We do not have the television equipment out. We've not had it out. We have not eaten at this point. I have a cold. I refuse to foul up our timeline at this point." There was a 35-second silence, then ground controllers changed the subject. Round one, to Schirra. There would be other arguments. Schirra would win most of them.

Later he obliged television viewers, holding a sign up in front of the camera that said, "Hello from the lovely Apollo room, high atop everything." It was the beginning of a new television series that would be dubbed, "The Wally, Walt and Donn Show." Said another sign in this first seven-minute look inside the cabin: "Keep those cards and letters coming in, folks."

Schirra, pressing through flight plan maneuvers and additional work sent up by the ground, shifted from the light-hearted to the bitter, all through the flight. Once, he criticized Mission Control for adding "Mickey Mouse" assignments to the flight. He was not alone. Cunningham, given another added duty, retorted, "We'll go on record here as saying people that dream up procedures like this after liftoff have somehow or other been dropping the ball for the last three years." Another change in rocket firing touched off Schirra. "That's your big mistake," he said, "in changing the rules in real time. I hope you learned a lesson from that." When a new man came on duty one morning, he greeted Schirra kiddingly, "Good morning, Wally. I was told I should be careful talking to you today."

Schirra kept up the criticism, spoke of "tests that were ill-prepared and hastily conceived by an idiot" and said, "We have a feeling that some of these experimenters are holier than God down there. We are a heck of a lot closer to Him right now."

Once he said, "You won't miss a hell of a lot if you don't get it here. We did not get the results that you're after. We didn't get a damn thing in fact." Again, he said, "I have had it up to here today, and from now on I'm going to be an onboard flight director for these updates, revised schedules. We are not going to accept any new games . . . or going to do some crazy tests we never heard of before."

There was one compromise. Although the colds were slightly better, Schirra was concerned about having access to their noses to clear their heads during the rapid pressure changes of descent. He asked that they be allowed to come down without their space suits on. The ground insisted the suits be worn, finally compromised on letting them come down without helmets or gloves. There was the chance of severe

Against Puffy Clouds—The Apollo 7 crew photographed the big Saturn 4-B rocket that entered orbit with them. They separated from this last stage of the Saturn 5, and played tag with it. Below is the Florida coastline from Flagler Beach south to Vero Beach.

ear pain unless the astronauts could relieve the pressure in their clogged Eustachian tubes.

But the landing was uneventful, and the spacecraft splashed down just one-third of a mile off its target in the Atlantic Ocean. In spite of all the bitterness, Schirra said, "The mission went beautifully." And mission officials were even more elated.

Apollo 7 was a textbook test flight. It also produced a number of firsts. Schirra was the first man to fly three times into space. Apollo 7 beamed back the first television from a manned U.S. spacecraft in orbit, something the Soviets had done repeatedly. It was the first three-man U.S. spaceship, something the Soviets had since Voshkod I. And Apollo 7 boosted the U.S. total of man-hours in space to 2,774, compared to 534 man-hours of experience for the Soviet Union.

"Apollo 7 goes in my book as a perfect mission," said Lt. Gen. Samuel Phillips, Apollo project manager. "In my experience this is the first space operation that's accomplished more than 100 per cent of its preplanned objectives. Our official count is that we have accomplished 101 per cent of our intended objectives."

One-hundred-and-one per cent. Machines performed well. Men meshed with machine. But after the flight some asked if too much had not been asked of the men. Certainly there were questions of how much men could do in space, how much could be crammed in a day, how men could be given enough sleep, saved the expense of unnecessary illness before flight, given food palatable enough so they felt less of a break in their eating habits.

But in spite of the stress on the men, Apollo 7 was a success. So much so that space officials were giving serious consideration to sending the next Apollo on an even more dangerous mission, more daring mission—a Christmas flight around the moon. No matter what the Russians were doing, the pressure was still on.

# 10 In The Beginning...

Four days before Christmas, 1968, the beaches of Cape Kennedy were crowded with tents and parked cars and people shielding their eyes against the sun to see the spikes of launch towers to the north. Especially one launch tower. This was not an ordinary shot. Disappointment and success flew together to create this day, and the days that would follow.

The lunar module that would ultimately carry two men to the lunar surface was lagging behind schedule. It was to have been test flown on Apollo 8. It was not ready. Apollo 8 was. The unqualified success of Schirra, Cunningham and Eisele instilled great confidence in the Apollo spacecraft. How best to capitalize on that success, to learn as much as possible for the moon landing, now a visible reality for the months ahead?

After their splashdown, the Apollo 7 crew flew to Cape Kennedy for conferences with space officials and the crew of Apollo 8—Frank Borman, Jim Lovell and Air Force Maj. William A. Anders. Lovell with Gemini 7 and 12 behind him was the world's most experienced space flier. Together with his Gemini 7 partner, Borman, they had more hours in space than the entire Soviet cosmonaut corps. Anders was a space initiate.

By mid-November, the space agency decided to go for broke with Apollo 8. It would fly to the moon, orbit it 10 times over the Christmas holidays, and head for home again. It would test the orbital mechanics necessary to approach the moon and would provide close-up looks with human eyes at the lunar surface. Intended or not, it also would give mankind a view of his planet and his silver neighbor in space that would thrill the world.

The stamina of the machine had been proved. There was extreme confidence in the stamina of the men who would fly it. Lovell, 40, had 425 hours and 10 minutes in space, the world record. Borman, also 40, had distinguished himself by taking a leading, effective part in the investigation of the Apollo fire. Anders, 35, was a Naval Academy graduate, a flier with 3,000 hours in the air, and an Air Force-trained nuclear engineer. Even though they had little time left to train for the mission, the space agency decided to press on. The pressure was on the crew and the men who would direct the flight from the ground.

Now, on this December Saturday, three astronauts became the first human cargo for the gigantic Saturn 5 rocket. For the first time, puny men were set against the immensity of the moon program. In the background was the Vehicle Assembly Building where the Saturns were prepared, a 52-story-high garage, the largest building in volume in the world. Next to it was the four-story launch control center with four separate firing rooms, three-and-a-half miles away from the launch complex for safety sake. To get Saturn 5 to the pad, it had to be carried by a treaded transporter as big as a baseball infield over a special stone crawlerway at a pace no faster than one mile an hour. The immense weight of the transporter and the rocket crushes the stone into pebbles as it rolls along.

Saturn itself—363 feet tall with the Apollo spacecraft perched on top, 60 feet taller than the Statue of Liberty, and fueled, 13 times as heavy. If it met disaster on the pad, its more than 5.6 million pounds of fuel would explode with the power of 610 tons of TNT in a spreading, lethal fireball. To protect themselves in Launch Control, they close the air conditioning vents nearly 10 minutes before launch. And because of that, there is no smoking at the launch consoles in those final minutes, until the rocket is on its way and the vents are opened again.

Men used to automobiles have been hard put to imagine the size and power of this project. But imagine, it would take 96 railroad tank cars to load the Saturn with fuel. The first stage fuel tank alone is large enough to accommodate three large moving vans side by side. The engines of that first stage generate twice as much power as all the waters of North America would if they were, at any given moment, channeled through power turbines. Now, on top of that rocket, put three men in a spacecraft for a trip around the moon.

It was a bright Saturday. The press stands were jammed. So were the bleacher seats at the Very Important Persons site, safely away from the launch pad. Among the 2,000 notable guests was Sen. Edward M. Kennedy, arms folded, passive-faced, squinting at the rocket standing on the space center that bears his brother's name. Beside him, his wife, Joan, brushing her blonde hair from her eyes and settling her dark glasses against the sun. There were senators and representatives, Supreme Court justices and foreign dignitaries. There was both envy and pride.

Half a mile away, in a private cluster, was a small group the space agency sought to shield from the others, unnoticed in the distance. There was Jim Lovell's wife, Marilyn, standing with a tall, lean 55-year-old man who once thrilled the world himself. Now looking like an aged Jimmy Stewart, Charles A. Lindbergh, his petite wife at his side, waited for yet another launching. The night before he had come out to the launch pad with a friend and stood watching, by the light of four dozen searchlights, the men at work on the Saturn rocket. He was a believer in rocket travel, a believer in adventure. After his pioneering single-engine airplane flight across the Atlantic 41 years before, he had turned some of his own money to the aid of rocket

For A View Of The Moon—Apollo 8 blasts off, shown here in a double exposure with its target, the crescent moon.

pioneer Robert Goddard. He had been to many launches at Cape Kennedy. But privately, because 15 years before he had turned his face away from the public arena. Now shy, retiring, he watched the fuming rocket with three men bound for the moon, and kept his own thoughts.

"Sixty seconds and counting as we come up on a flight to the moon," came the voice of Jack King over the loudspeaker. As the minute clicked away the events of the countdown, the crowd was nearly silent, as if their words could somehow make it fail. Suddenly, the words: "Ignition, we have ignition," and the burst of orange and yellow flame rising from the bottom enveloped the launch pad. After a silent moment of shock, the 2,000 spectators broke into a single, drawn-out "Ohhh." Then, voiceless, they watched the rocket rise off the pad on a pillar of flame and yellow smoke. All they could do was applaud. Seconds later, the Saturn drilling cleanly into the sky, the sound and shock struck and the applause was lost in it. Some held their ears, their eyes. But it seemed as if even the skin could hear. It was more than thunder, it competed with the heartbeat like a triphammer shudders pavement. Then, just as suddenly as it hit, it was gone. And they wondered at three men riding all that power to a place no one had reached before.

The Saturn 5 behaved perfectly. Borman, Lovell and Anders were in earth orbit, then they fired the third-stage Saturn engine again, boosting them into an orbit that would take them around the moon. The launch and its target caught the imagination of everyone. "Adieu Earth," said a German newspaper. "Today is the greatest day of the century." But some were more hard-headed. The most prophetic was Sir Bernard Lovell, director of England's Jodrell Bank Observatory, an expert in radio tracking of

Firing Room—Rocket expert Wernher von Braun (second row, second from right) watches intently as his big baby, the Saturn 5, hurls Apollo 8 toward the moon. His rockets pulled America from behind in the space race, and won the dash to the lunar surface.

Flying Away From Earth—Apollo 8's crew took this picture of the rounding image of earth, the United States southeastern coast and the Florida peninsula spread along the bottom, a great swirling storm center over the North Atlantic and the patchy blue waters of the Caribbean to the lower right.

space shots, American and Russian. Only unexpected setbacks, he said, would prevent the Americans from beating the Russians to the moon.

But, he said, it was important to consider just what the Russians thought the space race was. "If you're running a marathon . . . the person who gets to the first milepost doesn't necesarily win," he said. "And I would think that over the next decade or so, the Russians may have greater stakes in mind than simply a man on the moon. I'm thinking in terms of the further exploration of the solar system as a whole."

However little he thought of manned space exploration, his estimate of Soviet goals, and of American short-sightedness might be true in the future. And some of the observers at the VIP site watching Saturn that day would affect that future.

The Apollo 8 crew was moonward bound, and getting a view no man had ever seen. "Tell Pete Conrad he lost his record," they beamed to earth. Conrad had held the world altitude record of 851 miles set in Gemini 11. He had gone almost far enough away to see the earth as a complete globe, but not quite. Apollo 8 surpassed it already. "I'm looking out my center window which is a round window," reported Jim Lovell. "And the window is bigger than the earth is right now." He said he could see from South America to Florida to West Africa. "Good grief," said Mission Control, "that must be quite a view."

"Tell the people in Tierra del Fuego [at the tip of South America] to put on their raincoats," Borman called down. "Looks like a storm out there." "You care to give them a 24-hour forecast?" asked Mission Control. "Probably be as good as any they'd get on earth," Borman replied.

At home in Houston where she watched the launch, his wife, Sue, admitted her tension. "All through the week," she said, "he has tried very hard to instill in me the

The Dazzling Earth— The cheery home planet for Apollo 8 begins to grow smaller through the spacecraft window, and the Western Hemisphere shown here begins to fade in the distance. "How can we forget . . . ?" asked the Pope.

confidence he had. I certainly did pray. I say a lot of prayers. . . . If he had 10 launches, it wouldn't get any easier. The fact that they are going to the moon is very difficult for me to comprehend. I'd love to make a beautiful and profound statement, but I'm speechless. I'm emotionally drained."

For all their stated confidence, it was not easy on the astronauts. They were tired and short of sleep. They encountered some symptoms of the flu, or what they thought was the flu, on the first day out. Borman became so ill he vomited, had chills and other troubles. Despite all that, they beamed back their first TV show from space on schedule. "This program is coming to you from about halfway to the moon," Borman announced. They tried to show the earth to the people on earth, but all they could catch was a white blob about the size of a silver dollar. "It's a beautiful, beautiful view with a predominantly blue background and a huge covering of clouds," Borman tried to explain. The next day the pictures were better, and Apollo 8 climbed over the gravitational hill into the moon's sphere of influence. For the first time in history, earthmen were under the prime influence of the gravitational attraction of a celestial body other than their own.

Portrait Of The Moon— With the earth behind them, the Apollo 8 crew got this view of the moon and saw in it "a vast, lonely, forbidding place, an expanse of nothing . . ."

"We're looking ahead, of course, to tomorrow when we'll be just 60 miles from the moon," Borman said. "I hope you have everyone looking over everything very carefully." He said he wanted to know the spacecraft was in perfect condition before he used the spacecraft's rocket engine to slow his speed so that they would fall into orbit around the moon. The pictures beamed back to earth were spectacular. "You're look-

Sixty-Nine Miles Over The Moon—"They say there's a beautiful moon out there," said Mission Control. "That's a beautiful earth out there," said Borman, wistfully.

ing at yourself from 180,000 nautical miles out in space," Apollo 8 radioed. "I can pick up the southwest coastline of the Gulf of Mexico where Houston should be."

Borman, using binoculars to survey the earth and the dusk line where night pursues day, said, "We're looking at the United States right now, and there's a spectacular long, thin band of clouds. Looks like it may be a jet stream. It is absolutely spectacular, going all the way, or halfway around the earth."

The men on earth and in space were acutely aware that they were vying for the attention of a world preparing for Christmas, and relaxing with seasonal football games. Earlier in the month, a television network caught the devil from angry viewers when they cut off the last two minutes of a professional football game to begin a special children's show, "Heidi." A somewhat smaller storm of protest struck another television network the day before when a football game was interrupted for the first telecast of earth from Apollo 8.

Now, asked how the television show looked, Mission Control replied, "It was better than yesterday because you didn't preempt the football game." "Don't tell me they cut off the football game!" Borman cried. "You and 'Heidi' are running neck and neck in the telephone call department," the ground answered dismally. It was obvious as they approached the moon, they were running second to Santa Claus even in their own neighborhoods in suburban Houston. "You were upstaged by Santa Claus," Mission Control told Borman. "He came around on a fire engine just about the time you guys came on [television]. So most of the little critters were all outside."

In spite of that, the astronauts did their best to paint a picture of what they saw

A Sight For Mission Control—In Houston, the flight controllers watched closely as Apollo 8 beamed them their first close-up view of the moon.

from space, to give the earth a new perspective of their planet. Mission Control asked them for "as detailed a description as you poets can muster." Lovell tried.

"For colors, the waters are all sort of a royal blue," he said. "Clouds, of course, are bright white. The reflection off the earth is much greater than the moon. The land areas are generally a brownish, sort of dark brownish to light brown in texture."

Borman said he could see nothing on the night side of earth. "The earth is just too bright. Since this is winter time in the northern hemisphere, we can see all of the South Pole and the southern ice cap and not too much of the North Pole."

The world was watching Apollo 8, at least out of the corner of its eye. Warning that the Americans were taking unnecessary risks, Dr. Georgy I. Petrov, head of the Soviet Institute of Cosmic Research, nevertheless praised the American astronauts and wished them "above all, a successful return to earth." Pope Paul VI had more than praise.

"How can we forget," he asked the College of Cardinals with Christmas Eve approaching, "that while we sit here quietly, studying the horoscopes of the past and of the future, a feat which surpasses every ordinary limit of fantasy and human activity is being carried out in the cosmic spaces with the fabulous trip of three astronauts flying toward the moon?"

Christmas Eve, 1968, found the three crewmen rested and well, racing closer and closer to the moon. Mission Control counted down the dwindling mileage, and told the crew, "We have our lunar maps ready." Then, as the Apollo 8 turned the corner around the backside of the moon, the side never seen directly by the eyes of men before, their radio signals were blocked from earth by the lunar sphere. "We have loss of signal," Mission Control reported. For 10 anxious minutes, the earth awaited word that the crucial engine firing behind the moon had worked and the spacecraft was in lunar orbit. Suddenly Apollo 8 came from behind the moon and it was confirmed. "Keep a good eye on us," Borman said warily. In the hours that followed, the earth received televised pictures of the lunar surface, and a travelog narrative with it, and finally a Christmas message it would never forget.

Borman, a lay reader at St. Christopher Episcopal Church near his home, had hinted of the message before leaving earth, indicated it might be a plea for peace. "When we're finally up at the moon, looking back at the earth," he said, "all these differences and nationalistic traits are going to blend, and we're going to get a concept that this is really one world, and why the hell can't we learn to live together like decent people. I think this might be an appropriate season to go along with that."

Now whirling around the moon, the astronauts beamed back pictures of its craggy, pocked surface, from some 70 miles above.

"What does the old moon look like?" asked Mission Control.

"The moon is essentially gray," replied navigator Lovell. "No color . . . The Sea of Tranquillity doesn't stand out as well here as it does on earth. It looks like plaster of Paris, or sort of grayish beach sand," he said. "Whitish gray, like dirty beach sand with lots of footprints in it," said cameraman Anders.

"The moon is a different thing to each one of us," Borman added, as the image of the earth, tiny in the black distance, appeared on the television screens of the world. "It looks like a vast, lonely, forbidding place, an expanse of nothing . . . clouds of pumice stone."

Lovell saw the distant earth as "a grand oasis in the big vastness of space." Anders said, "You can see that the planet has been bombarded through the eons with numerous meteorites. Every square inch is pockmarked. Only the newest features have any sharp definition to them."

"It's not a very good place to live or work," Borman added.

They flew around and around, informally naming craters for themselves and a

Lunar Craters—Catching the light of the sun, losing their depth in shadows, the lunar craters stretched in every direction, betraying the eons of pounding the moon has received from space debris. The surface, said Apollo 8, looked like dirty, footprinted snow.

mountain for Lovell's wife, Marilyn. But the names were only in jest. The international organization which gives official names to lunar features passes out such honors posthumously. With those rules, it would, hopefully, be a long time before the moon bore the names of Borman, Lovell and Anders.

On the third orbit, Borman offered a prayer for peace, and asked Mission Control to pass a recording on to his church. "I was supposed to lay read tonight," he apologized. "I couldn't quite make it." Yet, he said, the prayer was not only for his church, but for people everywhere.

He prayed: "Give us, O God, the vision which can see Thy Love in the world in spite of human failure. Give us the faith to trust Thy Goodness in spite of our ignorance and weakness. Give us the knowledge that we may continue to pray with understanding hearts, and show us what each of us can do to set forward the coming day of universal peace."

After they had charted the possible landing sites for the men who would land on the surface, Anders called the backside of the moon unsuitable for a spacecraft landing zone. "It looks like a sand pile my kids have been playing in for a long time," he said. He has five children.

With Christmas Day approaching on earth, and the homes of the astronauts decorated with luminarias, the Mexican Christmas lights in which candles glow inside sand-filled paper bags, the astronauts sought to give the earth a greater notion of what they had seen, where they had been. They chose the first 10 verses of Genesis. While their television camera scanned the primeval, lifeless lunar desert that recalled a lifeless earth, Anders began: "In the beginning, God created the heaven and the

Fireball—Apollo 8 makes the hottest, riskiest re-entry yet, crashing into the earth's atmosphere at some 25,000 miles an hour. Airborne telescopic cameras caught its dash across the night sky.

earth. And the earth was without form, and void and darkness was upon the face of the deep. And the Spirit of God moved upon the face of the waters. And God said, 'Let there be light.' And there was light. And God saw the light, and it was good. And God divided the light from darkness."

Lovell continued, "And God called the light day. And the darkness He called night. And the evening and the morning were the first day. And God said, 'Let there be a firmament,' and God made the firmament and divided the waters which were under the firmament from the waters which were above the firmament. And it was so. And God called the firmament heaven. And the evening and the morning were the second day."

Then, from Borman: "And God said, 'Let the waters under the heavens be gathered together into one place. And let the dry land appear.' And it was so. And God called the dry land earth. And the gathering together of the waters He called seas. And God saw that it was good."

Then, the emotion of the day in his voice, Borman ended the telecast with this wish: "And from the crew of Apollo 8, we close with good night, good luck, a Merry Christmas, and God bless all of you, all of you on the good earth."

Below them, like an endless front lawn covered with dirty, foot-printed snow, the lunar landscape stretched on and on, blinding in the sunlight, forbidding and secret in shadow. Beyond, like a warm promise, the world they'd left behind glowed like a Christmas ornament, hiding in its colors a world of warm fireplaces, tables spread for Christmas, the comfort of home.

Around them, in the spacecraft, was the tight, little, ordered world of Apollo 8, the display keyboards, the circuit breakers, the switches and warning lights, the cold metal bulkheads and the contour couches, the checklists and the meals in plastic bags. There was one compromise to come this Christmas holiday, a dinner in the spirit of the season, a foil-wrapped portion of sliced turkey, to accompany the more modern foods. And from their friends, three airline-rations of brandy, the only alcohol carried into space from 233,000 miles away.

There were other comments that fed this unlikely Christmas. "They say there's a beautiful moon out there," said the voice of earth. "That's a beautiful earth out there," Borman replied softly.

"If you haven't done your Christmas shopping yet, you might as well forget it," said Mission Control. There was no reply from above.

The hints of loneliness came only in the small remarks, the things unsaid. Stowed in the lower equipment bay of the spacecraft were special tokens and charms carried into space to make them special gifts for the parents, wives and the 11 children awaiting the wonder of Christmas morning. Down there on earth, Marilyn Lovell spent Christmas Eve listening to her husband's broadcast voice. So did the other wives. Sue Borman began the evening by getting her hair done for church Christmas morning. Alan Anders, 11, already had tried out a new Christmas rod and reel on nearby

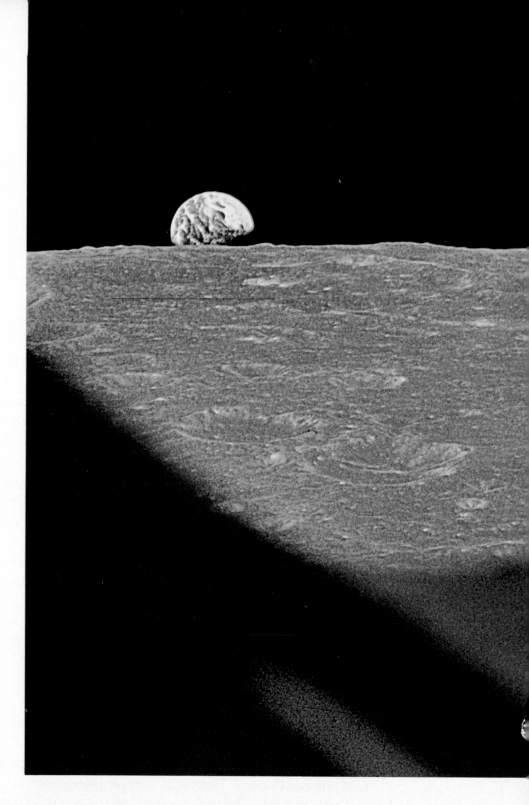

Earthrise—The first astronauts to see the earth rising over the lunar horizon, Borman, Lovell and Anders never tired of the view. It was Christmas Eve and back home the world was full of warm thoughts and feelings.

Taylor Lake. Jeffrey Lovell, 2, opened his presents on Christmas Eve with his brothers and sisters, and received, among other things, a toy helicopter.

But in Apollo 8, the big preparations were for the Christmas morning firing of the spacecraft rocket that would send them back to the planet where Christmas began.

Borman took note of the condition of his crew after the tiring day, made sure the spacecraft was flying true, and scrubbed the rest of the flight plan before the rocket firing. He would stay up and babysit the spacecraft while Lovell and Anders slept.

With the crew awake in the early hours of Christmas Day, the astronauts were be-

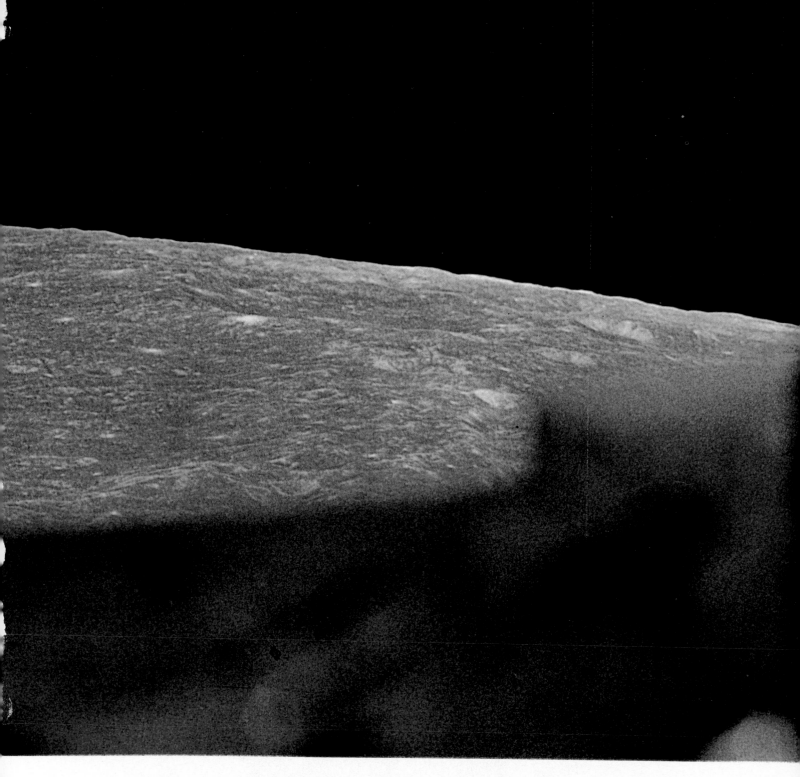

hind the moon again in radio silence. They were due to come out the other side, heading home. Then they were overdue to come out the other side. For almost six scary minutes there was no Apollo 8. Then there was Lovell's voice.

"Please be informed, there is a Santa Claus," he said. "The burn was good." They were homeward bound. On earth, Christmas morning dawned with great relief. Sue Borman went to church and heard her husband's tape-recorded voice, and those of his crewmates, reading Genesis from the moon. It was a small congregation, a short service. After, she was handed the tapes by the pastor. Outside the church, her blonde hair holding its own against a brisk Christmas breeze, she clasped the tapes to her breast and smiled. "These are my first Christmas presents," she said. Remembering the voices beamed down to earth, she added, "It's just what this small world was waiting for."

She was postponing most of the Christmas present opening until her husband returned, she said. "We'll be each other's Christmas presents."

Marilyn Lovell wore her Christmas present to church. It was a new mink stole she found mysteriously under the tree. "It came from the man on the moon, whoever that is," she smiled. "That's what it said on the package." The night before, when she heard her husband's voice say, "Please be informed there is a Santa Claus," she added gratefully, "I always knew there was one." Jeffrey Lovell's new toy yellow helicopter didn't last through the service. He broke it during his fidgeting. Valerie Anders gave thanks at Roman Catholic Mass. Her husband was carrying her Christ-

mas present aboard Apollo 8. It was a specially-made pin, a gold numeral 8, crested by a moonstone with an azure lapis lazuli at its base.

The small crescent moon hovering in earth's skies, and the feat of Apollo 8 could not be ignored. Radio Havana called the flight "cosmic" and rebroadcast a Voice of America description of it, including the voices of the astronauts. It was the first time Radio Havana had broadcast any program by the U.S. agency.

A Japanese newsman, in Houston to cover the flight, awakened a space agency public information officer in the small hours of the morning to ask if the Apollo 8 Christmas message was in the flight plan. It was. "Can I obtain a script?" asked the newsman. "Yes, where are you?" the space agency officer asked. "In my hotel," was the reply. "Well, then," said the officer, "reach into your bureau drawer. There is one there." Amazed, the newsman looked, and found a Gideon Bible.

If other flights had evoked the polite congratulations of governments, this one reached the people. In Moscow, a Russian turned to an American and said, "It must be great to be an American tonight." In Tokyo, a fifth-grader said, "When I grow up I can visit the moon thanks to Apollo 8's pioneering orbit around the moon." In Rome, an elderly woman turned to an American and said, "Magnificent! Splendid! Signor, my compliments." In Paris, a Frenchman said, "I've never had any particular love for Americans, but I'm really happy with their success. The American did everything in the open, not like the others. You can only put your hopes with theirs, and now congratulate them."

As always, there were detractors. "Why go to the moon?" grumbled one Muscovite. "We have troubles enough on earth." A German wine salesman said, "It would be better if the Americans used some of that money for building hospitals or cleaning up cities." A Swiss pensioner said, "A mad way to spend money."

New York offered a tickertape parade, and Mayor John Lindsay said, "You have unlocked the door of the universe and held it open for all of us." President Johnson said, "You have made us feel kin to those Europeans five centuries ago who first heard news of the New World. You have seen what man has never seen before."

Apollo 8 splashed down in the mid-Pacific west of Christmas Island after the hottest, fastest re-entry to date. The pilots did not fire braking rockets this time, but used a narrow channel of the earth's atmosphere to slow the spacecraft's 25,000-mile-an-hour speed. They landed at night, and bobbed on the ocean surface as recovery forces waited until dawn before closing in and picking them up. Borman, kidded about his light beard, shaved it off in the helicopter. When he was asked what the moon was made of, he said, "It's not made of green cheese at all. It's made of American cheese."

ome For New Year's— orman at the microphone, nders and Lovell are ack on earth after the neliest Christmas yet round the moon. Speaking the men of the recovery arrier *USS Yorktown,* orman admitted he naved aboard the covery helicopter. He referred to because his eard was so light he ways took a kidding oout it from his Apollo crewmates.

# 11 An American Moon?

It began to look more and more like an American moon.

Apollo was in high gear. The Soviet effort was flagging.

Apollo 8 had visited the moon for the first time and returned safely.

Borman, Lovell and Anders, three minds, three pairs of eyes, raised on a live planet amid green grass and trees, tides and seasons, saw what looked like a dead planet close-up, photographed it, measured its gravity, a lumpy kind of gravity that disturbs the neat mathematical circles spacecraft fly in.

Apollo 8 helped answer some human questions. How much work can you pile on men in space? How much pressure can they take and still perform efficiently? Why do so many experienced fliers become spacesick, queasy in orbit? Lovell seemed to have the answer to that one. Rapid movement in weightlessness makes you seasick. Take it slow and easy until the eyes and ears used to earth gravity adjust to a world without top or bottom.

Apollo 8 also convinced some who thought men in space was a foolish endeavor. In London, British astronomer Sir Bernard Lovell softened his earlier opposition. "Viewing the moon from only 70 miles away," he said, "must be regarded as one of the historic moments in the development of the human race."

Twelve years before, the United States started second in this new endeavor of mankind. Now it was unquestionably first. In fact, the race to the moon began to look like no race at all.

The Soviet Union had been strangely erratic, its space program full of starts and stalls. Two months before Apollo 8, on October 25, 1968, the Soviets launched their first Soyuz spacecraft in the 16 months since Komarov's death. It was unmanned. The next day, they sent up a second Soyuz spaceship, this one piloted by cosmonaut Georgy Beregovoy, in an obvious space hunt for the first ship. He found it and maneuvered to within 650 feet of his target, but did not close and dock.

Twice, in earlier unmanned flights, the Soviets had performed automatic rendezvous and docking experiments with Cosmos satellites. But now it appeared they were having trouble mastering the techniques developed in the Gemini program by U.S. space pilots.

At the same time, some were asking whether Soviet difficulties might not be as much political and economic as technical. Leading Soviet scientists made unusually nonpartisan remarks about the U.S. space successes. One said that the Soviet Union would welcome the results of the Apollo 8 flight because the information it yielded would help the Soviet space program. This same scientist said that a major difference between the Soviet and U.S. programs was that the Russians wanted wholly automatic control systems to back up their manual systems, while the United States gives "very complicated activities to the astronauts themselves."

Another Russian scientist said his nation did not believe it was necessary to put heavy emphasis on manned flight until unmanned satellites had been used to the utmost for scientific information-gathering.

The statements seemed to echo similar arguments in official Soviet publications. Some Americans wondered whether it was sour grapes, a sort of apologia should the Americans land first on the moon. Some guessed that the Soviets were putting moon landings second to earth-orbiting spaceships which might have greater military value. And some asked whether, after Komarov's death, the Soviet Union decided for political reasons to slow its manned space flight effort because of the great expense involved, and because of the possible blow to its technical prestige involved in failure. No one knew the answer.

But Sir Bernard Lovell suggested one—that the Soviet Union viewed the space race as a marathon, and aimed at long-term exploration of the solar system rather than a one-stop dash to the moon.

The Soviet Union clarified its standing in January, 1969. It hurled two Soyuz spacecraft into earth orbit—and this time there was union. Indeed, there was more than that. The two Soyuz craft not only linked together, but there was crew transfer between the two. First up in Soyuz 4 was Lt. Col. Vladimir Shatalov, followed a day later by Soyuz 5 with Alexei Yeliseyev, Yevgeny Khrunov and Boris Volynov aboard. They found each other in space, docked, and Yeliseyev and Khrunov transferred over to Soyuz 4.

For the Soviets, it was a great leap forward in fashioning orbiting earth stations—and it showed they still intended to go to the moon, or the planets, by way of such platforms circling the earth. The Americans, using a lunar orbit to reach the lunar surface, were still ostensibly ahead, but it was fair warning that the Russians weren't far behind.

In the United States, there was no longer any question that the Apollo command ship was ready. The Saturn 5 rocket was ready. The last question-mark was the lunar module, a bug-like contraption meant to land two men on the moon and carry them back again to an orbiting mother ship. It had to work perfectly, or the first two men to step onto the moon would be left there forever.

The crew chosen to test the lunar module for the first time trained hard. Two were veterans of Gemini flights. Jim McDivitt had flown Gemini 4 on Ed White's pioneering U.S. space walk. Dave Scott had flown with Neil Armstrong on Gemini 8. Russell L. Schweickart, the rookie civilian astronaut with red hair, had not flown yet, but he

would make a space-walking debut on Apollo 9. The three astronauts would rehearse the vital moon landing techniques in the neighborhood of the earth, and prove out the lunar module in close proximity of the mother planet, where rescue was easier, and risk slightly less.

Apollo 9 was a test flight. On the surface it had little of the glamour of Apollo 8. But its dangers were just as great. It was the next step before the lunar module could be tested near the moon. "We could get stranded in lunar orbit," said one flight engineer speaking of the future. "But, hell, we could strand men in earth orbit too."

Despite the less dramatic aspects of Apollo 9, it put extreme pressures on its crew. Its flight plan was jam-packed. The training for it was high-key. As the launch day approached, doctors found they had three sick astronauts on their hands. For the first time in 18 man-in-space flights, a launching had to be cancelled because of illness. McDivitt, Scott and Schweickart were all suffering from stuffed noses, sore throats and exhaustion. For the last weeks before the launch date, they had been putting in as many as 18 hours a day training for the flight, most of that time in spacecraft simulators. In the end, it was their health that broke down. The common cold caused a delay of three days and cost the space agency half-a-million dollars. But as chief flight surgeon Dr. Charles A. Berry explained, "The only thing I could guarantee is that we would have three sick astronauts if we launched Friday."

Berry had been warning that the pressures on the men were too severe both before and after the flights. "I feel strongly about this," he said. "We've had 100 per cent post-flight illness on these Apollo flights. I don't think we've got a spacecraft that carries germs around and infects them. And I can't see where the Cape has changed that much from the days of Mercury and Gemini. What has changed is that the complexity of the flights has increased so, that the crew has got to put in considerable training and long hours and they don't get enough rest.

"You take a crew which starts out a flight tired," Berry added, "and you give them demanding tasks in a new environment without adequate rest, you bring them back, debrief them for 10 days. Then you put them out with thousands of people, and with their resistance low, they contract illnesses."

All three Apollo 7 astronauts developed colds in space, and other astronauts developed minor illnesses. All six Apollo astronauts to date had fallen ill after their return to earth. It was a measure of how hard the job was. It was also a lesson in how hard the men could be pushed; obviously harder than their bodies would stand.

Flight operations director Kraft also looked at the mission critically. "This is an extremely complex mission," he said, "probably one of the most complex we've flown. It would probably not surprise any of us if we did not come out with 100 per cent success. But we have every confidence that we have an opportunity to."

Finally, on March 3, 1969, Apollo 9 thundered off into earth orbit. Behind them, in a garage-like compartment in the third stage of the Saturn 5 rocket, was the lunar module. Once in orbit, they separated from the third stage, turned around and docked nose-to-nose with the lunar lander and pulled it out of the garage. Safely away from the still-loaded third stage rocket, they watched as the ground fired it up and sent it

Take Me To Your Leader—The Apollo 9 astronauts, McDivitt, Scott and Schweickart, walk to the van that will take them to their spacecraft. The closer they got to the moon, the more they looked like creatures of space.

into an orbit around the sun. "It's on the way," Scott called out. "It's just like a bright star disappearing in the distance."

In the next days, the astronauts tried a number of maneuvers. They wagged their rocket engine to test how much bend there was with the two spacecraft joined. They found it was "solid as a rock." They also found the spacecraft as crowded as the flight plan. One encumbrance was the big black hoses supplying them oxygen through their spacesuits. "Have you ever been attacked by a band of wild elephants?" McDivitt asked Mission Control. "Have you ever dreamed about octopuses?" Scott added. At one point, they complained of the jammed flight schedule. "We were pretty well crowded today to get all these things in," one of them said, "and we sort of missed lunch."

To make identification in space easier, the astronauts named their lunar module Spider, and their command ship Gumdrop. On the third day of the flight, McDivitt

The Lunar Lander—
The first test of the lunar excursion module, photographed from the command module.

and Schweickart entered Spider through the docking tunnel in the Apollo 9 nose, and once there, they tested the major descent engine on the lunar module, the engine that would slow its descent to the moon, allowing it to land gently. There was one problem. Schweickart became sick to his stomach before the day's events began, another episode of space-sickness from rapid movement in the weightless environment.

Despite this, the astronauts gave the earth a televised look at the interior of their lunar module. But it came across like a silent movie. The astronauts were tired, and the communications were bad. By the end of the busy day, they were running an hour behind in their flight plan which is timed to the clock. And Schweickart was feeling out of sorts. In a private conversation with doctors and flight controllers on the ground, he said he had no appetite and was not in top condition. He had encountered two spells of nausea in the course of the day, vomiting and feeling dizzy. McDivitt decided to cancel the space walk, limiting Schweickart's duties to what the 33-year-old flier thought he was up to.

The Command Module—The astronauts in the lunar lander caught their home away from home in this shot against the background of earth.

The next day, feeling better, Schweickart joined McDivitt in entering the lunar module again. Then the rookie, who became an astronaut only after the height limit was raised to 6 feet, stepped out into space, 140 miles above the earth, and using the handrails, climbed around the joined spacecraft. He carried the radio code name "Red Rover," and carried on a hide-and-seek dialogue with McDivitt (Spider) and Scott (Gumdrop).

Through it all, Mission Control tried to raise them, but they didn't answer, absorbed in what they were doing. "Hey. Anybody up there read me? This is Houston."

"Oops, there goes a nut," said Gumdrop, standing in the open hatch of the command ship and watching debris slip by him, flying into space.

"You talking about me, Dave?" asked Red Rover, now hanging by one hand on the exterior of the lunar module. He had strengthened his hands in training by squeezing steel springs.

"Why don't you wave your hand at the camera, or something?" asked Spider in the lunar module trying to photograph Red Rover.

"Hello there, camera," Red Rover teased.

"Dave, come out, wherever you are," he shouted mockingly.

"Man, we're all taking pictures of everybody taking pictures," Gumdrop replied. "Everyone brought their cameras from home."

"Oh shoot," said Red Rover, having difficulty handling his. "If it ever works again it'll be a miracle. It just got smashed around."

In between lines, Red Rover was taken with the panorama spread before him, the blues, whites and browns of earth turning slowly in the sunlight, a child's ball rolling along an endless dark field. "Hello dere," he said in wonder. "Boy, oh boy, what a view! There's the moon right over there."

Then Gumdrop got playful. "I'll send something out there, and we'll make a satellite," he told Red Rover, who was standing on the front porch of the lunar module, his feet fixed in anchors called the golden slippers. Gumdrop tossed an unidentified flying object out of the hatch. "There it goes," he said, "right between your legs."

"My heavens!" Red Rover shouted in mock alarm. Looking back at the command ship, he saw even more debris flying into space. "David?" he called. "Things are still falling out of there. What are you doing? Throwing everything overboard?"

McDivitt, the veteran who remembered Ed White's reluctance to get back in, saw that the spacecraft was cutting toward the night side of earth. He was boss. He gave Schweickart a 10-minute warning. Then, he said, "Okay Rusty, why don't you start coming back in now?" Red Rover was reluctant, but he answered, "Coming back in."

Mission Control, happy with the 38-minute space walk and relieved that it was over, broadcast over the airwaves for all to hear, "You heard it here, live, firsthand, the adventures of Red Rover and his friends, Gumdrop and Spider."

Back inside, the astronauts were McDivitt, Scott and Schweickart again. The flight reverted to the seeming monotony of space maneuvers. Schweickart's space walk had proven that the handrails and other restraints greatly eased the job of working in

Like Kids At Play—David Scott is standing in the open hatch of Gumdrop while Rusty Schweickart takes his picture from the front porch of Spider. Below, the Mississippi River rolls on.

Prospecting The Earth—Apollo 9, using special infrared cameras, scanned southern California and northern New Mexico. Red areas are healthy vegetation in the Imperial Valley below the Salton Sea, a favorite astronaut landmark.

space, and yielded confidence that spacemen could be rescued from the lunar module if, for some reason, it could not be linked up with the command ship. The space walk was trimmed to allow for an earlier rising the next day, and even more crucial tests of the lunar module.

Again, Schweickart and McDivitt entered the lunar module, and this time they separated from the command ship. It was a rough undocking. Then the two space-craft hovered near each other, the proven command ship, the unproven lunar lander. "You've got a nice looking machine," Scott said, giving it the once over. "And that's all it looks like too; some kind of machine."

With a series of rocket burns, they moved away from each other, into different orbits, testing the lunar module's descent engine, a rocket with a throttle that could adjust its power to the rate of fall. Finally, out of sight of each other, more than 100 miles away, McDivitt jettisoned the descent stage of the lunar craft, the portable launch pad that would be left on the moon's surface when the men who land on the moon head for home. Now, armed only with the ascent engine, he burned off in pursuit of the mother ship, mimicking the rendezvous that would take place 69 miles

Red Checkerboard—The irrigated fields along the Colorado River come out in red in another infrared photo showing heat radiation. Perhaps one day man will survey his crops and forests from space.

above the moon's surface, four months hence. Steering by radar, then by sight, McDivitt and Schweickart flew the lunar module, or what was left of it, back toward Scott in the command ship. When Scott caught sight of the lunar module with his two erstwhile companions aboard, he smiled, "You're the biggest, friendliest, funniest-looking spider I have ever seen."

McDivitt had trouble orienting the mother ship against the glare of the sun off the earth's surface. The dialogue told more of these risky minutes, the emotions in their voices becoming stronger the closer the two spacecraft got.

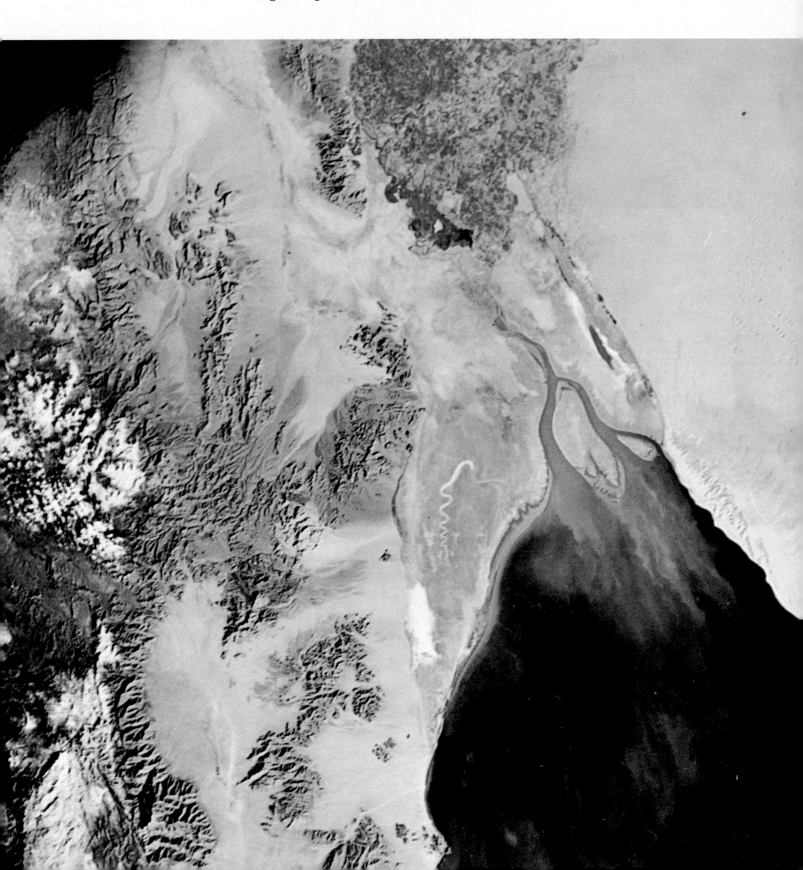

"My good friend in the Gumdrop over there can see me again," McDivitt told Mission Control. "I'm in the daylight."

"Okay, Spider," Scott said. "I have you against the earth background. That thing is really travelling."

"One of us isn't right side up," McDivitt said in a world that has no right side up. "I can't see you in there, Dave."

"Oh, I'm in here," Scott assured.

"Let's stick together," said Spider. "I'm with you," said Gumdrop.

Then when they finally docked, smoothly, with scarcely a bump, McDivitt heard the docking signal and exploded with relief. "Wow, I haven't heard a sound like that in a long time," he sighed. "I have capture."

"Okay, Houston," Scott confirmed. "We're docked."

"Hey," Schweickart called down to earth. "When I take a break, I'm going to bed for three days." "We concur," said Mission Control. "Three days off."

"Is that Saturday, Sunday and Christmas?" a tired McDivitt asked sarcastically.

It worked, nearly as flawless a performance as anyone dared hope. The two craft that would take men to the moon and home again, the procedures, the stamina of the men themselves, all of it spilled confidence over the men in Mission Control. Now the pilots separated from the moonship for the last time, and the ground triggered the lunar module's engine for the last time and sent it flying off into space, little more than an orbiting garbage can for Apollo 9. The spacemen had stowed debris in plastic bags inside the craft before it was jettisoned. "It's going like mad," Scott reported. "It's really moving out."

Moonward Bound—The earth recedes in the distance, a child's ball in the sky, as Apollo 10 streaks for the moon.

"I hope I didn't forget anything aboard it," said lunar module pilot Rusty Schweickart. "We do too," said Mission Control, adding they hoped no one forgot the lunar module pilot.

"I didn't forget him," McDivitt interrupted. "I left him there on purpose."

Apollo 9 was a success, and the way was now open to test the lunar module in the neighborhood of the moon.

While Apollo 9 was still in space, there was an important administrative change in the space agency. James Webb, a Johnson-appointee and a Democrat, had stepped down from the job as administrator early so that the space agency job would not become a political issue in the middle of the Apollo program. Deputy administrator Dr. Thomas O. Paine had been acting administrator during the changeover to the Nixon administration. For months the 47-year-old deputy handled the top office in the space agency while the new President sought another man to take over. The son of a retired Navy commodore, and once a Navy submarine officer and deepsea diver himself, Paine came to the space agency from General Electric's Center for Advanced Studies in Santa Barbara, Calif. Finally, President Nixon, unable to find another suitable candidate, elevated Paine from his temporary post to head of the space agency. Nixon said he named Paine after he "searched the country to find a man who could take this program now and give it the leadership that it needs, as we move from one phase to another."

Paine promptly forecast the accomplishments of the second decade in space would surpass the accomplishments of the first.

The lessons of Apollo 9 were not lost on the men preparing for Apollo 10. The Apollo

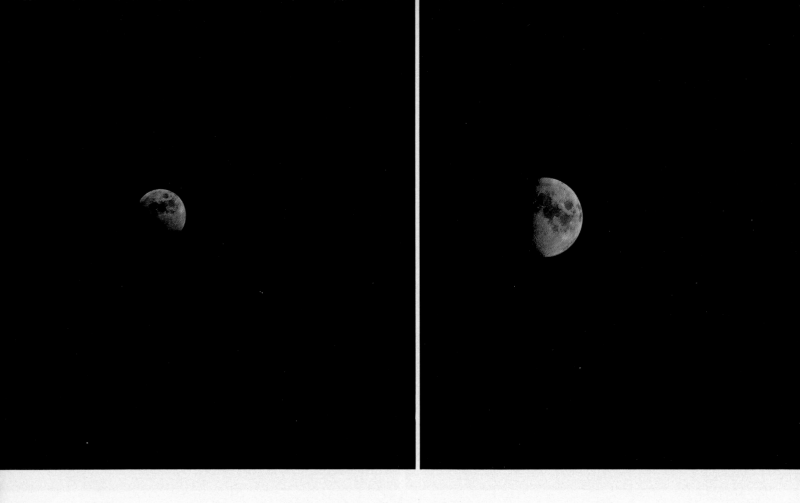

program pressed on, but the first real compromises were made in the pressures put on the crew. As flight surgeon Berry insisted, training schedules were eased. Hopefully, there would be no more $500,000 colds. In the days before their May launch, the Apollo 10 crew worked no more than six hours a day. They were given free time to trot and bask on Cape Kennedy's broad beaches. "We're not going to get in a rundown condition where we're more susceptible to illness," said command pilot Tom Stafford.

Weeks before, when training pressures were still high, both Stafford and lunar module pilot Gene Cernan fought off bouts with the flu. Command module pilot John Young managed to avoid the illness, despite the close contact between them. "He's stubborn," said Cernan.

All three men were space veterans. Young, sometimes called a loner with a reputation for quiet wit, was copilot with Gus Grissom on Gemini 3, and command pilot on Gemini 10. Gene Cernan was the space walker who flew with Stafford on Gemini 9. In his two tiring hours out among the stars he discovered some of the difficulties of working in weightlessness. He returned to the spacecraft early with a fogged visor. An easy-going pilot who likes to putter in his garden, Cernan was a late entry in the space program. Like Stafford, he had to wait until the height limit was raised to 6 feet before he was admitted. He is married to a former airline stewardess who learned to fly because her husband was a flier.

Stafford, a textbook flier and extrovert, married his high school girl friend, who taught him how to drive a car. He graduated near the top of his class at the Naval Academy, later entered Harvard's graduate school for business administration. He left after only three days to answer the call to the astronaut corps.

The Moon Beckons—As Apollo 10 nears, the moon loses its mystery and shows its pocked face born of millions of years of violence. It isn't a pretty place.

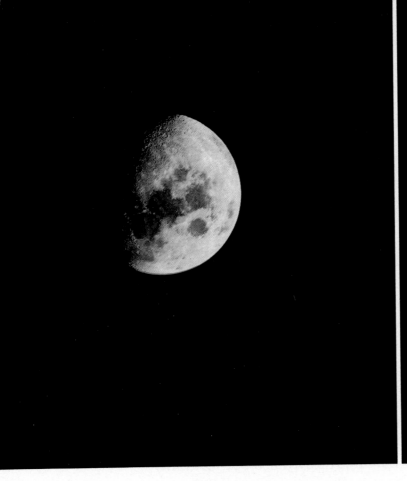
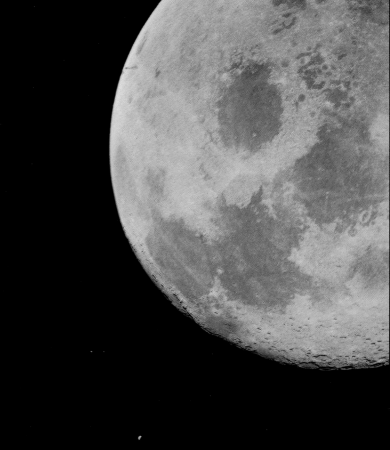

Stafford and Young, whose birthdays are only a week apart, were 38. Cernan was 35. They functioned well as a unit. As Cernan once put it, "Because we're different types of personalities is probably why we get along so well. We're not three one-man astronauts, and we're not two guys and one guy, or one guy and two guys. We're three guys that have a great deal of confidence in each other."

The Apollo 10 crew had one other singular attribute. In the months before the shot they got the reputation as salesmen for the space program, aware of public apathy, but with a public relation man's sense that the adventure was worth selling to the American people. Well before the launch, they announced that they would use their color television camera—the first carried into space—to show as much as they could of what they saw. "We want to share it with you," explained Cernan, "because then you can see what's behind the 'gee whizzes' and 'oh gollies' that we speak of during the flight."

There were rumors in the first months of 1969 that the Apollo 10 crew was campaigning actively to change their flight plan into the first lunar landing mission. It wasn't to be. They would follow the careful, step-by-step mission profile set for them. They would blast out of earth orbit, slow into lunar orbit, then send two men, Stafford and Cernan, on a close-up inspection trip only 10 miles above the lunar surface. It would measure the uncertainties in the lunar module and check out the landing runway for Apollo 11. But Apollo 10 would not land itself.

A talkative crew, they dashed into space on May 18, into orbit around the earth. Then, firing up their third stage of the Saturn again, they were moonward bound at nearly 25,000 miles an hour. Watchers in Australia saw the spacecraft moving like a star reflecting the glint of the sun's rays. When they fired that engine, one Australian reported, "It lit up a ninth of the sky."

The only wife to see the launch at the Cape, Barbara Cernan watched and waited with her 6-year-old daughter Tracey. "It's like having a baby," she said. "You know what to expect, but you never get used to it." Cernan, told by Mission Control that the rocket blast "really rattled the cages around here," said, "I would have liked to have seen the expression on Tracey's face on that one."

Coming out of earth orbit, following the moon-flight pattern, the Apollo 10 crew nosed around and pulled the lunar module out of its garage in the third stage of the Saturn. Then, on ground command, the now useless rocket was fired again, joining some 40 other spent spacecraft in orbit around the sun.

The astronauts looked back at earth, now growing smaller in their windows, the layers of clouds, the oceans and continents in distant relief. "You blink your eyes and look out there, and, you know it's three dimensional," Cernan marveled. "But it's just sitting out there in the middle of nowhere. It's unbelievable . . . Just for the record, it looks like a pretty nice place to live." The voices from earth agreed.

En route to the moon, the astronauts beamed back color television views, boosting their TV time from a planned 15 minutes to 72 minutes. It played hob with network television schedules. But the views were fascinating. They focused on the lunar module they had nicknamed Snoopy, joined nose to nose with their spacecraft they named Charlie Brown. They showed the earth rolling in the heavens. Through the clouds, they said, "We can see the Rocky Mountains sticking out . . . Can't tell if you have any smog in L.A. or not. But Alaska is pretty much socked in." Then, for fun, they beamed to earth recordings of Stafford and Young playing guitars and all three singing, "Up, Up and Away." Mission Control didn't know about the tapes, had not expected the serenade from space. "I thought the song was very appropriate," Cernan radioed. "We had some trouble stowing the bass drum aboard."

"Somebody's voice is changing," countered Mission Control. "Either that or you've stowed somebody else aboard."

Even though they were heading for man's closest visit to the moon, they could not get over the receding view of earth. "Looking from this distance," Stafford said, "you could never tell anybody could inhabit the place." And Cernan added, "We're sitting here, and it's almost like science fiction looking back at it."

It was like science fiction, but Young had a more practical comment. "One of our problems," he said, "is trying to figure out which way is up and which way is down." He was upside down at the time, from an earth point of view. As the miles to earth increased and the miles to the moon dwindled, Stafford reported, "Hey, we finally got a good view of the moon. It's kind of nice to know where we're going."

On they went, out of the prime reach of earth's gravity into the domination of the moon's pull, over that invisible hill, speeding up as they headed for the backside of the moon. "In about 15 minutes," Stafford said, "we will pass into the shadow of the moon." They were three days out from earth. For some 27 minutes they would be out

Earthrise—The earth rises over the bleak horizon of the moon. It is a warm sight.

of radio contact, blocked from their home planet by the lunar sphere. In that time, the spacecraft rocket engine would have to fire precisely to slow them into lunar orbit. Mission Control waited for the spacecraft to come out from behind the moon. Then it was there. "You can tell the world," reported Stafford, "we have arrived."

"It was terrific to hear their voices," said Barbara Cernan. Mrs. Frank Borman, who had been through it before on Apollo 8, dashed across the street to the Young home and hugged Barbara Young. "Where have you been?" Mrs. Young said happily. "Wringing my hands," said Sue Borman. The two women later stood watching the quarter moon over Houston. "I think I see them," kidded Sue Borman. "Boy," said Barbara Young wistfully, "it sure would be nice to see them."

The Apollo 10 crew kept up a running commentary of what they saw. "Boy," said Young, "this moon is lit up like a Christmas tree on the dark side. I don't mean with lights. But it sure is brightly illuminated from the earth." It was the second firsthand report of earthshine lighting up what from a distance is the darkened part of the moon. The astronauts also told of some differences in color to what the Apollo 8 crew saw. "The color looks like a brownish gray to us," Young said. But Apollo 8 commander Frank Borman, watching the view on color television on earth, stuck to his report that it was mostly black and white.

"Looking out at some of the mountains we see, it's going to be a real trick to go down there tomorrow," Stafford said. "We can pick out a couple of good little volcanoes." Cernan, who would make the close-up trip with him, said, "Now we're in pitch blackness although you can still see the lunar horizon against the black sky. It's

Forbidding Landscape—From some 70 miles up, the astronauts photographed
this grim panorama of Crater 302 on the backside of the moon, a face it never
turns toward earth. How did it all begin?

Crater—The Apollo astronauts stared into the depths of lunar craters and wondered how old the torn lunar surface was. It would take lunar explorers to find out.

a black moon that you can't really see anything on. But there is a definite distinguishable horizon against the black sky where the stars are coming up."

The critical moments would come the next day. The first trouble came with Cernan and Stafford in the lunar module called Snoopy, and Young in the spacecraft called Charlie Brown. They had already had pressure troubles in the tunnel connecting the two. In correcting the trouble, the docking rings holding the two craft together were twisted out of alignment slightly. As they disappeared behind the moon, Mission Control warned the astronauts not to separate Snoopy from Charlie Brown if the alignment twisting increased. There were more tense minutes before Apollo 10 came in radio contact again, and tracking stations saw two separate objects coming from the moon. They were undocked. Now the most critical time for Stafford and Cernan began. They fired the descent engine on Snoopy to change their orbit and bring them within airliner altitude of the moon's surface. Firing the rocket just three seconds too long would send them crashing into the lunar mountains rising 30,000 feet high. But the rocket burns were perfect. The bug-like lunar module zipped down for the lunar landing site at some 3,700 miles an hour.

"Hello Houston, this is Snoopy," the voice rang out. "We is going. We is down among them, Charlie." The excitement burst from their voices. At one moment there was a profane phrase, but the astronauts stopped talking abruptly. "We're right there," they called down. "We're right over it . . . I just wish we could stay."

"Oh Charlie," they radioed, "we just saw an earthrise, and it's just got to be magnificent." Stafford began a detailed description of the landing site. "There are enough boulders around here to fill up Galveston Bay," he said. Close-up, he said, "They do have different shades of browns and grays here. It's like vulcanism. There is also a pure white near the edge . . . and we see some large boulders that are black to blackish gray."

They tested out the landing radar, whisking over the tortured lunar surface. "Also," they said, "it looks like we're getting so close all you have to do is put down your tail wheel and we're there."

"Okay," Stafford reported, "We are coming up over the site. There's plenty of holes there. The surface is actually very smooth, like a very wet clay . . . with the exception of the bigger craters."

Two hours later, as they headed for the intended landing site for the second time, Stafford and Cernan set themselves to jettison the descent stage of Snoopy, legs, rocket and all, and fire the ascent stage to rendezvous with Charlie Brown again. Then it happened. Just as the two vehicles separated, the men in the ascent stage were thrown wildly by a wobble action.

"Son-of-a-bitch," shouted Cernan. In the scary seconds that followed, he shouted to Stafford to "hit the AGS," bringing into play the abort guidance system. Stafford hit the switch and the ascent stage stabilized. "I don't know what the hell that was, baby," Cernan told the ground. "But that was something. I thought we were wobbling all over the sky."

They were indeed.

Return—The lunar lander comes home to the mother ship after its close-up look at the moon. It had jettisoned its descent rocket and the spider-like legs when it shot up to rendezvous with the command module.

(On earth, the astronauts were criticized for their profanity. Finally, they made up a sign which they hung at Cape Kennedy: "The Flight of Apollo 10: For adult audiences only.)

The wobble was traced to an omission in the flight plan which left two control systems in force, an error made by someone on the ground. But the quick-wittedness of the pilots had countered the trouble, brought it under control.

The command ship was circling in an orbit 69 miles above the surface. Now, Snoopy rose to meet it. The rendezvous and docking that started so full of danger ended perfectly. "Man, we is back home," said Stafford. "Snoopy and Charlie Brown are hugging each other," cried Young. "That rendezvous was the best we've ever had," Stafford added. "We were right up the tail all the way."

Later, they sent Snoopy on its way into a lonely, useless orbit of its own. Cernan saw it roaring off to become another satellite of the sun. "I feel bad about that," he said. "He's a pretty nice guy. He treated us pretty well."

Snoopy gone, Charlie Brown began the long trip home alone, a restful, uneventful trip, beaming television pictures to earth along the way. There were a number of lessons learned, lessons that could delay the lunar landing of Apollo 11.

One was the close-up look of the landing area in the Sea of Tranquillity.

"It looks a lot smoother than some of the photos show," Stafford said. "I estimate a 25 to 30 per cent semi-clear area. So if the LEM [lunar module] has enough hover time, it should not be a problem. However, if you come down in the wrong area and you don't have hover time, you're gonna have to shove off."

Could the lunar module of Apollo 11 come in clean enough to find a boulder- and crater-free area for its four-foot fall to the surface? Could the insulation, pressurization, radar and power problems be solved before July? Those questions remained unanswered as Apollo 10 whizzed home to its perfect splashdown.

Arriving at earth just before dawn, it appeared as a star in the sky over the Pacific Ocean. Tracking cameras followed its glowing course, saw for the first time the super-hot re-entry, the drop from 400,000 feet, the parachutes, the splashdown and the recovery of the astronauts. It was all beamed to the Western world on television, making Apollo 10 the most completely viewed flight in history.

But for all the openness, for all the views from space, the critical questions awaited the dialogue between the flight controllers and the men who were up there. On Launch Pad 39A, waiting, as it had since before Apollo 10 roared off from a sister launch pad nearby, was another Saturn 5 rocket with the Apollo 11 spacecraft on top. And unwritten history waited with it.

Color TV From Outer Space—Color television casts from outer space were instituted during the Apollo 10 mission. To demonstrate weightlessness on one TV cast, astronauts Tom Stafford, left, and John Young, right, sat in opposite positions. This is how it looked on home TV screens.

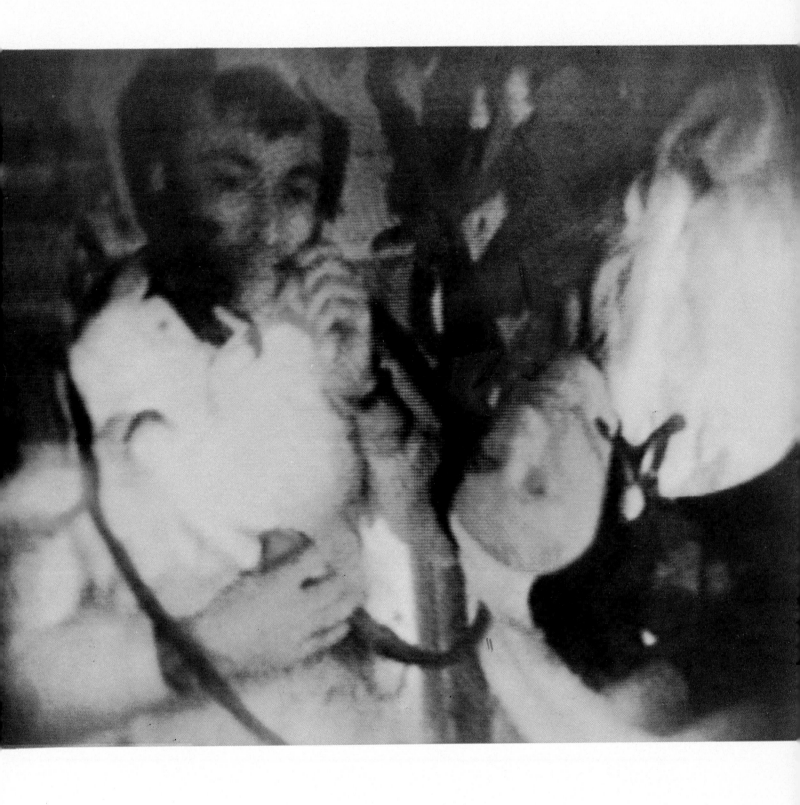

# 12 Footprints On The Moon

And, of course, always there was the moon, and with it, unwritten history. Perhaps the story of Creation itself.

Always the moon, staring out of everyone's sky. Nothing has so captured the eye and mind of man. She stands, as always, large on the horizon, shrinks in her zenith. On hot muggy nights, she flames as orange as the sun rising from the ocean. On blue summer days, her ghostly crescent haunts the daytime sky. She is a pristine silver ball in the clear desert night, small and alone. She conspires with the sun to order the tides of earth's oceans. Yet the simple cycle of her passage keeps time with the metabolism of mice and fiddler crabs. The sun gives man day and night. The moon gives him weeks and months. So many things tick to the lunar clock. What makes the grunion run? What times the rise of human fertility? What brings the rock crab ashore to feed? What alone eclipses the sun? The moon. The moon. The moon.

Poets sing of her. She is Shelley's "orbed maiden," Shakespeare's "inconstant moon," Emerson's "tinsel" in the sky. Almost every adjective, metaphor and rhyme keeps her company. Songwriters saw a "moon river," a "moon over Miami," a "Cuban moon," and "that old devil moon." Mark Twain wrote, "Everyone is a moon and has a dark side which he never shows to anybody."

July, 1969. There was a dark side to the earth, too. The placid moon looked down on a blue-green planet where men ached over the troubles of their world and dreamt of the stars. There was still a war in Vietnam, still poverty, still hunger, still racial unrest and student unrest, still a cold war, still ballistic missiles and anti-ballistic missiles. There was also still the moon.

The moon lives in a thousand primitive legends, a thousand pagan religions, goes by a thousand names. Early men saw the hunter's moon and found her the haven for all kinds of animals, even a toad. Others, afraid of the night, made her the home of crises, dreams and tranquility. The Eskimo believed her the runaway sister of a sorcerer. The Greek called her Selene. The Romans called her Diana, the twin sister of Apollo. If that were so, they were to be together again.

Ancient superstition held that the full moon summoned forth the werewolves.

Modern criminologists say there is a rise in the crimes of passion with the full moon. But perhaps the poet Francis Thompson caught her true personality. "The innocent moon, which nothing does but shine," he wrote, "moves all the labouring surges of the world."

Some believed staring at the moon brought on madness. Others thought witches could call down vapors from the moon to do their evil work. Scientists, looking at her upside down through glass, conjectured. Johannes Kepler, 17th century German astronomer, thought there were creatures on the moon. A modern scientist suggested that the lunar soil, brutalized by the sun's heat and the frigidity of space, was in chemical balance so tenuous that a man's footsteps could trigger a monstrous fire. Others guessed that the moon's surface was covered with dust so thick it would swallow a man or a spaceship.

One by one, the theories died the nearer man got to the moon. They died just as surely as Galileo's telescope killed the notion the moon was a polished globe in the sky. The first pioneer probes, like groping fingers of man, reached out for the moon but never made it. But Soviet Luniks did. They crashed into her, circled her, followed by Ranger probes. Surveyor space machines soft-landed on the moon. Lunar Orbiters photographed her every face. From 69 miles out, Apollo 8 found her only black, white and gray, like dirty, footprinted sand. Apollo 10 came closer, to within nine miles, saw rugged landscapes reminiscent of the southwestern desert and badlands, mountains, and brownish soil.

July, 1969. The moon was no longer a total mystery. As Neil Armstrong said, Apollo 11 would not be a flight into the unknown. The moon had been measured, compared and poked at. She was more a small planet than a moon, the largest of 32 moons that shadow the nine planets of the solar system. She measured 2,160 miles in diameter, 6,790 miles around the waist. She was less dense than earth. Even though she was one-fourth the size of earth, she had only 1/100th the mass. Her gravity was one-sixth as strong as earth gravity. A 150-pound earthling would weigh only 25 pounds on the moon. She was a lady of extremes. Her day was 14 earth-days long. Under the beam of sun and the emptiness of shadow, her temperatures ranged from 243 degrees above to 279 degrees below zero.

For all the small physical facts, there were larger questions that persisted. How did it all begin? There were three prime theories: that the moon erupted out of the earth, thrown off by centrifugal force when the earth was spinning faster; that both bodies formed at the same time, condensing out of the primordial gases of creation; that the moon was a wandering planet captured by earth's gravity. Daughter? Sister? Captive wife?

Those questions remained unanswered as Apollo 11 readied for flight. They were part of the reason for going.

Thus in July, 1969, as always, the moon, strange foreign body in earth's sky. Against the new image of her bleak craters and mountain ranges the world considered three men—Armstrong, Aldrin and Collins.

The Rocket And The Dream —Apollo 11, bathed in searchlights at Cape Kennedy, waits with the target of man's quest gleaming in the night sky.

Armstrong, Collins, Aldrin—One would wait above while two walked the moon.

Armstrong would be the first to touch lunar soil. Born Neil Alden Armstrong on August 5, 1930, in Wapakoneta, Ohio, he was the son of a traveling state auditor. He worked as a teen-ager for 40 cents an hour, saved his money to fly for $9 an hour. He got his pilot's license at 16, before he got his driver's license. He won his Bachelor of Science degree in aeronautical engineering from Purdue, his Navy wings from Pensacola. He attended graduate school at the University of Southern California. In the Korean War, he flew Panther jets from the carrier Essex; once nursed a crippled plane home; was shot down behind enemy lines and rescued, ran up a total of 78 combat missions. After the war, he joined the space agency and flew the rocket-powered X-15 to heights of 200,000 feet, speeds of some 4,000 miles an hour. Blond, blue-eyed, 5-feet-11, 165 pounds, married, the father of two boys. He became an astronaut in 1962, brushed with death in the Gemini 8 flight, again when his lunar landing trainer crashed. Sparing of words, direct, with an engineer's analytical mind, dry humor, boyish smile. He was Apollo 11's commander, a civilian, the highest paid man in the astronaut ranks at some $30,000 a year.

Edwin E. Aldrin Jr. would be the second man to the moon's surface. He was an Air Force colonel, and the son of an Air Force colonel. His father was an old-time aviator and friend of Orville Wright, Robert Goddard and Charles Lindbergh. At 73, the elder Aldrin still held a pilot's license. His son was born January 20, 1930, in Montclair, N.J. The proud parents nicknamed him "Buzz." His mother's maiden name was Marian Moon. A so-so student in grade school, Aldrin finished third in his class of

475 at West Point, and won his Doctor of Science degree from the Massachusetts Institute of Technology. His thesis was on orbital rendezvous and laid out that technique for the Gemini program. He flew 66 combat missions in Korea, was credited with two MIGS. He became an astronaut in 1963. Unlike Armstrong, he is an exercise buff, pole vaults in his backyard, jogs, does push-ups, scuba-dives. He holds two honorary degrees, is a 32nd degree Mason, a Scout merit badge counsellor, an elder and trustee of the Webster, Tex., Presbyterian Church, the father of two sons and a daughter. Thinning blond hair, blue eyes, 5-feet-10, 165 pounds. On Gemini 12 he became the champion U.S. spacewalker, helped solve the fatigue problem of working in space. He studied geology to better judge lunar rocks, was known as the best scientific mind in the astronaut corps. Taciturn, seemingly arrogant and curt to some he considers of lesser intellect, deep of voice, short of patience with what he considers inane questions, another man of few words. He is a heavy reader of technical journals, not a man of the arts. He avoids the company of his wife's amateur theater group. Devoutly religious, he works late at night, again the analytical engineer's mind dissecting a problem until it doesn't exist. Efficient, a perfectionist, precise. One who knows him says, "Ever hear of a comedian, or entertainer who is always 'on'? Well, Aldrin is a professor who is always on."

Before the flight, Aldrin, a man of challenges, said, "We have been given a tremendous responsibility by the twists and turns of fate. I think it's difficult to cite previous examples of challenges that have been so tremendous for individuals to face."

It Was Real!—They were going to the moon! Armstrong leads the way to the van that will take them to the rocket.

Michael Collins, no middle name, no middle initial. He was assigned the job of flying protective patrol in the mother ship orbiting the moon while his two crewmates descended to the lunar surface. Born in Rome, Italy, October 31, 1930. His father was an Army major general, and his uncle, Gen. J. Lawton "Lightning Joe" Collins, was a World War II hero and eventually Army chief of staff. Mike Collins' older brother is an Army brigadier general. Collins was a West Point graduate and an Air Force lieutenant colonel. Brown-haired, brown-eyed, 5-feet-11, 165 pounds, a test pilot, the father of two girls and a boy. He flew Gemini 10, walked in space between his Gemini spacecraft and the flying Agena rocket, rode the docked Agena like a cowboy. He was first assigned to fly Apollo 8, but noted that his legs were becoming weaker, became so bad he would fall down. It took two dangerous operations to correct the bone spur and disc pressing on nerves in his upper spine. He missed the chance to be on Apollo 8's trip around the moon. But then, he was assigned to Apollo 11. Considered a poet among astronauts, certainly of a whimsical bent. Maybe the Irish in him. An Episcopalian, married to a Roman Catholic, his children are Roman Catholic. Imaginative, talkative, the odd man on Apollo 11. Relaxed, active sense of humor, easy to like, embarrassed by philosophical questions, embarrassed by the position fate has put him in. He made it clear to newsmen in a gentle way to take it easy on his family when he was gone. But on the other hand, a good test pilot, competitive, aggressive, an avid handball player without much challenge at the Manned Spacecraft Center. He enjoys playing with his children and tending the flowers of his garden.

Fate and schedules brought these three together, this month, of this year. In history, they would never be separate again.

Armstrong and Aldrin, of course, held the choicest seats. Collins held the doubtful honor of being their chauffeur. Actually, for him, it was even more ignoble than that. "I'd like to point out," he said at a news conference before the flight, "...that I have no TV set on board and therefore I'm going to be one of the few Americans who is not going to be able to see the moon walk. So, I'd like you to save the tapes for me, please. I'd like to look at them after the flight."

Meanwhile, another U.S. astronaut, Frank Borman, was touring the Soviet Union as an emissary of the U.S. space program. He told the Russians he was working on a program in which the United States hoped to launch a large space station in a few years. "I foresee a time in that program," he added, "when Soviet and U.S. spacemen will be flying together."

Even while Borman was there, there were widespread rumors the Soviets would launch a rocket to the moon July 12, perhaps to steal thunder from the U.S. flight.

At first, it seemed as if the American public was dulled to the coming event. Men were going to the moon. Men were going to land on the moon. Men were going to walk on the moon. Impossible! The incredibility of it! Much of what discussion there was had a negative tinge. A Harris poll found less than half the American people in favor of shooting men to the moon. It wouldn't work. Couldn't work. Shouldn't work. Yet, bit by bit, the realization grew. It would be tried.

"Go Baby Go!"—Automatic camera catches the Saturn-Apollo express to the moon from the top of the gantry at skyscraper height.

In Worcester, Mass., Mrs. Robert Goddard sighed and said, "It's been such a long time coming. My husband would have been beside himself with delight." On the eve of Apollo 11, she recalled her life with the man who pioneered rocketry as the Wright brothers pioneered aviation. "His dream couldn't change," she said. "Everything he did was aimed at the achievement of space flight. I think how he felt was best explained by an entry in his diary—it was so many years ago. He said, " 'When old dreams die, new ones come to take their place. God pity a one-dream man.' "

Harry F. Guggenheim, now president and editor-in-chief of *Newsday*, recalled how various Guggenheim family funds had aided Goddard's work, how Charles Lindbergh had acted as liaison between the Guggenheims and Goddard. He also recalled a letter Goddard wrote to H. G. Wells in 1932. "How many more years I shall be able to work on the problem I do not know," Goddard said. "I hope as long as I live. There can be no thought of finishing, for aiming at the stars, both literally and figuratively, is a problem to occupy generations. So that no matter how much progress one makes, there is always the thrill of beginning."

Goddard died in 1945, one month short of 25 years before the scheduled flight of men to the moon. He lived in ridicule, withstood names like "moony" and "crackpot." But his work laid the foundation for modern rocketry.

The Apollo 11 astronauts broke their rigid training schedules to spend the Fourth of July weekend with their families in Houston, the last time they would be together before the launch. On July 10, the countdown began on the Saturn 5 rocket and the Apollo spacecraft. The astronauts announced that they had chosen the radio call sign Columbia for their spaceship and the call sign Eagle for the spindly-legged lunar lander. Columbia and Eagle. To many, it sounded almost corny.

The day after the countdown began, President Nixon announced he was regretfully canceling plans to dine with astronauts before the flight. Actually, doctors had ruled against the meeting, afraid the astronauts might pick up a stray germ that could develop into a full-blown infection during the mission. Borman, then at Cape Kennedy, was strong in his criticism of space agency doctors for killing what he considered a prime morale booster before the flight. But Apollo 11 was carefully built on the experience gained in other flights. As much as possible, personal contacts with other persons was limited, and the training pace was slowed in the weeks before the flight to allow the astronauts time for rest and relaxation to keep them fresh for the coming rigors. On Sunday, July 12, the Russians launched a spacecraft, Luna 15, to the moon. It was unmanned. Its purpose was not announced.

The Apollo countdown proceeded almost flawlessly. At times it was ahead of itself, and had to hold for real time to catch up. Launch was scheduled for 9:32 a.m. Cape Kennedy time, July 16, a Wednesday. The public fever, the realization of what was coming, began to rise. Noticeably in the last days before launch, traffic became heavier in the Cape Kennedy area. Flight schedules were filled. Campers, trailers, out-of-state license plates began to appear on the streets. Rent-a-car companies pulled in vehicles from all over Florida and still couldn't find enough. Motels, hotels and apartment

From Gibraltar To Cape Town —The shrinking image of earth seen from moonbound Apollo 11 shows a clear day over Africa from the Mediterranean east to India, south to the Cape of Good Hope.

house owners boosted rents, some as high as $60 a night. The Chamber of Commerce predicted over a million people would be in the Cape area on launch day. There were worries over whether there would be food supplies enough to feed them.

Foreign nations seemed to grab the excitement sooner than America did. Venezuela and Brazil announced that church bells would ring on the day the Americans set foot on the moon. Venezuela considered making the day a national holiday. The U.S. Embassy in Rio de Janeiro set up a huge television screen in the Museum of Modern Art, and the museum planned to stay open all night. The Colombian government asked television manufacturers to set up TV sets in all the town squares, and students in Bogota were given the day off. In a continent where soccer is king, all soccer games were cancelled in Colombia for the day the astronauts would reach the moon. Stores in Japan were flooded with models of Apollo 11 and one Japanese television announcer planned to live in a guarded hotel room, wearing a space suit and eating space food until the Americans blasted off from the moon again. A Yugoslav newspaper offered an $800 prize for anyone who could predict man's first words from the moon. And in London, David Threlfall of Lancashire, a science fiction buff, got ready to collect $24,000 for the $24 he bet at 1,000-to-1 five years before that man would reach the moon before 1971. He had two years to spare.

At Cape Kennedy, the day before the launch, all public parks had been converted into camp grounds and trailer parks. In nearby Titusville, youngsters roped off their front yards and charged a dollar a head for tourists to watch the blastoff from lawn chairs. Some 30 police boats cruised the Banana River which runs toward the Cape to monitor the hundreds of boats arriving to see the shot from offshore. Motels had no-vacancy signs up in a 50-mile radius of Cape Kennedy.

Everyone seemed to be getting on Apollo 11's bandwagon. One man was jogging the 1,000 miles to Cape Kennedy from Houston to demonstrate for physical fitness. A Houston fireman was bicycling the same route to carry a certificate making the Cape Kennedy fire chief an honorary member of the Houston Fire Department. The Rev. Ralph David Abernathy led a contingent of the Poor People's Campaign in a march on the Cape led by a mule-drawn farm wagon to symbolize man's inability to solve the problems of poverty and hunger on earth while he reached for the moon. Tuesday night, Abernathy told a church rally in nearby Cocoa, "I'm proud of those three men, the astronauts." Then he led 300 marchers to City Hall. "America has mixed up priorities," he said. "I'm happy because we're going to the moon, but I'd be a little more happy if we had learned to live down here on earth."

Pope Paul addressed himself to the Apollo flight for the second time in four days. He asked everyone to pray for the American astronauts on their way to "the pale and silent satellite of the earth."

The time was drawing near for the astronauts. A rainstorm hit Houston the night before the launch and knocked down an exhibition tent at the space center and a tree in Mike Collins' yard. Rocco Petrone looked at the ticking clock and said, "We have had a very smooth countdown. There has not been any problem whatsoever that

First Step—Armstrong's blurred image seen by the Eagle's camera.

would scratch us." From the astronauts' quarters, Armstrong said, "We are not unduly fatigued and we're ready to fly." But mission director George Hage warned, "Anytime you have a space vehicle with many million parts, there are a lot of elements that have to work right. Nevertheless, project officials have done everything man can do to minimize the chance of failure."

On hand for his first personal view of a launch, former President Johnson made a short luncheon speech the day before the flight. The waiting, he said, was "kind of like standing around the hospital room before your first baby is born. You know you must be prepared to accept the worst, but you hope for the best." Looking at the 12 years that had brought the nation to this point in space flight, he said, "If we can lead the world to the moon, we can lead them to peace and bountiful prosperity here at home."

President Nixon made a five-minute telephone call to Armstrong, Aldrin and Collins from his White House office. "You carry with you a feeling of good will in this greatest adventure man has ever undertaken," he said. Their space journey would, he said, "lift the spirits of the American people and the whole world."

That night, while technicians pumped 525,000 gallons of liquid hydrogen and liquid oxygen into the fuming Saturn rocket, the astronauts had a steak and mashed potato dinner and went to bed about 9 p.m. They were awakened at 4:15 a.m. Wednesday, July 16, to begin their final preparations. They had the traditional breakfast of steak,

Second Man On The Moon—Buzz Aldrin climbs down the ladder to take his first step on the moon. Armstrong warned him of the long last step from the bottom rung to the surface.

eggs, toast, coffee and orange juice at their quarters five miles away from Pad 39A and their rocket. They had a quick medical exam in which they were proclaimed "rested, fit as a fiddle and ready to go."

On launch day, the National Council of Churches issued a nationwide call to prayer for the astronauts. And at Gate 3 of Cape Kennedy, the Rev. Abernathy led a small contingent of his Poor People's Campaign to a meeting with the space agency chief, Dr. Thomas Paine. Paine told Abernathy, "We feel the space program is a program for all Americans. We don't regard it as a program against the antipoverty program. We'd like to see you hitch your wagons to our rockets and we hope the space program will encourage this country to tackle other problems," he added. Then he invited Abernathy and some of his followers to watch the blastoff from the VIP stands, and Abernathy accepted the invitation. In the stands, it looked as though the seat of government had been moved to Cape Kennedy. With former President Johnson, there was also Vice President Spiro T. Agnew, head of President Nixon's Space Council. Space agency protocol people fretted over a visitor's list that included ambassadors and congressmen, Cabinet members and business leaders. But there were no representatives of the Soviet government, although it seemed for a while there would be. All invitations were ultimately declined.

To Catch The Sun's Wind—Aldrin sets up the metal foil sail to catch the wind of subatomic particles blown out from the sun.

Outside the gates, civil defense officials estimated the throngs in the Cape area at over a million. Sheriff's deputies in Brevard County guessed there were some 700,000 over the normal population of 230,000. Certainly there had never been a crowd that large in the area before, not for John Glenn, not for anyone.

Traffic was heavy even inside the Cape Kennedy gates. The astronauts were a trifle

late arriving at the rocket. The countdown clock moved inexorably on. Over the loud-speaker at the Cape, public affairs officer Jack King looked out at the hot, humid sands, the palmetto, the rocket pointing at the nearly cloudless skies and said, "It is a beautiful morning for a trip to the moon." Over the communications loop, test conductor Paul Donley signaled the end of the beginning. "Good luck and God speed from the launch crew," he said. "Thank you very much, we know it will be a good flight," Armstrong replied.

There were three small men laying back in their couches in that tiny chamber on top of the Saturn rocket. It was real. They were going to the moon. In the White House, President Nixon watched on television, and with him to provide insight and narration was Apollo 8 commander Frank Borman. The only wife of the Apollo 11 crew at the Cape to see the launch was Janet Armstrong. She watched from a boat in the Banana River.

King's voice quickened with the final minutes of the countdown: "Two minutes and 10 seconds and counting and the moon at this precise second is 218,986 miles away." He was watching the plotting boards and computer screens flashing green in the launch control firing room. Launch director Petrone, who headed the 450-men crew at their consoles, could feel the tension in the room like crackling electricity.

Forty seconds...thirty...eight, seven, six, five, four, three, two, one. "We have ignition." Great storms of burning fuel, orange and red in the gray-black smoke, billowed out of the rocket, while 50,000 gallons of water a minute sprayed through the

Tranquillity Base—Aldrin scouts the footprinted lunar soil, his nation's flag standing taut on the airless plain.

By The Dawn's Early Light—Armstrong holds the staff at left while Aldrin adjusts Old Glory's furls on a wire support in the glare of the lunar sunrise.

holocaust. For almost nine seconds, the rocket stood there bathed in its own flame as the five Saturn engines built up thrust—thrust more powerful than 92,000 locomotives or 500,000 automobiles; thrust enough to reach for the moon. Then, the four 20-ton restraining arms fell back and Saturn and Apollo were released. Gulping 15 tons of fuel a second, the 363-foot rocket stirred, lifted agonizingly off the pad.

"And we have liftoff."

We have liftoff. For one brief shining moment, all of mankind had liftoff. Over 500 million people saw it, felt it. Millions more heard it. The ridiculously tiny televised image of that monstrous rocket and its shattering roar filled the human eye and ear. If there were doubts, there were none now. If there were detractors, there were none now. The aim was the moon. The singular men involved, the spaceship handcrafted by thousands, the rocket, all were instruments of history. And never before had so much of the human race been privy to history; not the windless morning Columbus sailed with the riches of Isabella, not the foggy morning Lindbergh throttled up to face the Atlantic, not the frigid morning Robert Falcon Scott pressed into the Antarctic. But this warm, humid morning in Florida . . .

"Go baby go," the voices rose from the VIP stand, from those who could find voice. Most stood, speechless, as the pulse of the rising rocket shook the earth they stood on, the air they breathed. In 12 seconds, the onboard guidance system ordered the rocket to tip slightly to the southeast, out over the Atlantic.

Nearly Done—Aldrin's job nears the end, the experiments and the flag to be left on the moon in place.

"Wow, what a ride," came the word from Apollo 11. "It's really moving, babe." But mostly their voices were flat, unexcited, full of the mechanical details of the moment. "We've got a roll program," Apollo 11 reported. "Roll complete and pitch is programmed."

"You're good at one minute," said Mission Control. "Thrust is go all engines. You're looking good." The first stage burned for some two-and-a-half minutes, then cut off, separated, and the second stage took over.

Forty miles high, cutting wing-like shock waves in the thinning air. Then after 11 minutes, 53 seconds of powered flight, in orbit around the earth. Parked, so to speak. Ready to blast off again for the moon. On earth it was a time to catch breath. The Rev. Abernathy led his group in the VIP stands in singing "We Shall Overcome." Then, to newsmen, he said, "As I saw the rocket take off—I've always loved my country —the pride that I felt for it made me forget momentarily the two worlds of America. I forgot for a moment, the world of racism and poverty." Former President Johnson said, "You never get the same feeling sitting in a room watching it on camera that you get when you're right there. . . . We haven't reached the end. It's just the beginning. Decisions made 12 years ago made possible what we saw today." He said as the rocket rose he could sense "half a million people were there lifting." Recalling that President Kennedy made his pledge to go to the moon only eight years before, Johnson said, "If we can do all that in such a short time, I wonder why we can't put the same effort into peace for all time." Vice President Agnew proposed that America choose a new and more daring goal in space, the planet Mars. If America doesn't, he said, "someone is going to do it."

Armstrong, Aldrin and Collins, in orbit around the earth, were silent, busy with the preparations to fire the third stage rocket again and break the grip of earth's gravity. Everything had worked perfectly thus far. Their launch was just 724-thousandths of a second late. Said Mission Control, "It couldn't have been more accurate." Two-and-a-half hours later the third stage fired again and hurled them toward the waxing crescent moon "You're on your way now," said Mission Control.

The Soviet news agency *Tass* reported the Apollo launch briefly just a few minutes after it occurred. But at the same time, the Russians remained silent on the mission of Luna 15, moonward-bound and well ahead of Apollo 11.

Now, the spaceship Columbia separated from the third stage rocket, turned around and docked nose-to-nose with the moon-lander, Eagle, stored in the garage-like hull of the third stage. After the Eagle had been pulled free, Mission Control vented fuel from the third stage, now useless, and sent it into orbit around the sun. Columbia and Eagle were alone at last for their trip to the moon.

Six hours after the launch, his confidence buoyed by the smoothness of the operation, President Nixon proclaimed Monday, July 21, a Day of National Participation, and urged the nation to watch Armstrong and Aldrin walk on the moon. "In the past ages," he said, "exploration was a lonely enterprise. But today, the miracles of space travel are matched by the miracles of space communications; even across the lunar

distance, television brings the moment of discovery into our homes, and makes all of us participants."

The Apollo 11 astronauts wasted no time making the people of the world participants in their adventure. Armstrong looked out at the shrinking earth and reported, "Out my window right now I can observe the entire continent of North America, Alaska, over the Pole, down to the Yucatan peninsula, Cuba, the northern part of South America, and then I run out of window."

From some 60,000 miles out, the astronauts aimed their color television camera out the window and gave the earth a spectacular 15-minute view of itself. The picture, taped and telecast later to the nation, showed mostly the Pacific Ocean. "Hey, Houston," Buzz Aldrin asked from space, "Do you suppose you could turn the earth a little bit so we could get a little bit more than just water?" "I don't think we've got much control over that," said Mission Control. "Looks like you'll just have to settle for water." Seven hours into the flight, Aldrin shed his heavy pressure suit, and an hour later, so did Armstrong and Collins. It had been a long day, but the astronauts said they were in fine shape and had taken no medication. Everything had gone so smoothly, they were ahead of their flight plan again. Mission Control gave them permission to go to sleep two hours early, while it kept watch by instruments on the ground.

In Wapakoneta, Ohio, where they named a street Neil Armstrong Boulevard, one resident said, "Now that he's on his way, there's nothing we can do but wait. His fate is in the hands of God, the crew and the equipment." In Washington, Mrs. Nixon said, "It went off so beautifully—and with it my prayers." In Cairo, Egypt, Sheik Ahmad Haredi, the Moslem world's leading moon expert, approved of Apollo's flight and observed, "The Koran urges Moslems to look up from their earthly abode to what lies beyond the moon and stars." In Lagos, Nigeria, one man worried in a letter to the editor of the *Daily Times* that Apollo might blot out some of the moon's light that comes to earth. In Munich, West Germany, the Bavarian state mint began striking gold and silver coins engraved with the names of the three astronauts and: "The First Man on the Moon, 1969. Space Belongs to Everyone. God Created It." In Dacca, Pakistan, a boy born an hour after launch was named Apollo. In Vincennes, Ind., two parents named their newborn son Neil. In El Lago, Tex., just before dark, Janet Armstrong arrived home from Cape Kennedy and faced newsmen wearily. "I don't feel historic," she said. So ended Day One on the trip to the moon.

Day Two began with more checks on the spacecraft. Armstrong and Collins reported they slept seven hours each, Aldrin only five-and-a-half. Columbia and Eagle, still nose-to-nose, were 113,270 miles from earth. Their original speed of some 25,000 miles an hour, nibbled away by the drag of earth's gravity, had dropped to 3,289 miles an hour.

In Moscow, it was rumored that Luna 15 would soft-land, scoop up some lunar soil, and head back to earth with the first samples of the moon. If so, it would steal some of the glory from the American flight.

Suspicion of the Soviet aim deepened when Great Britain's Jodrell Bank Observatory

Reflections Of History—Armstrong, the first human to step on the moon, and the Eagle that carried him there, reflected in Aldrin's visor.

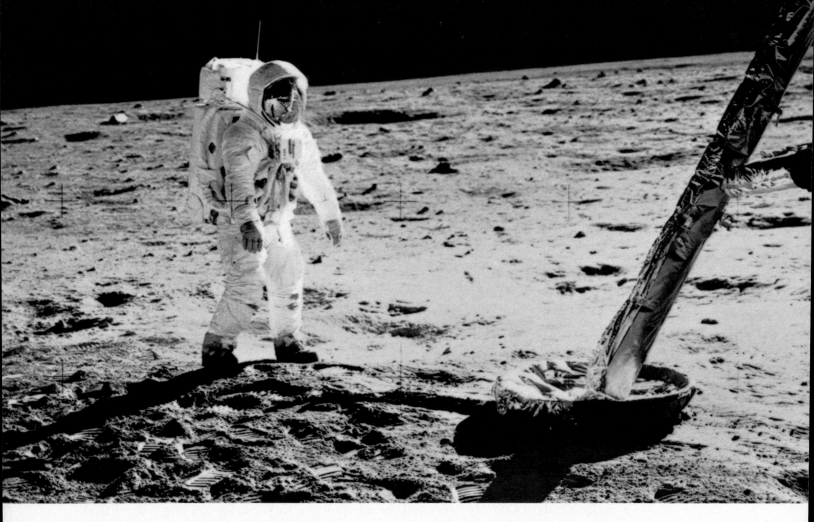

reported that the robot spaceship had gone into orbit around the moon. The size of the orbit indicated also that the Soviets planned to land Luna 15 on the moon's surface. Some U.S. experts doubted the Soviet craft capable of a return to the earth. First, they said, it was unlikely that Luna 15 could blast off from the lunar surface with enough power to reach earth because it just wasn't big enough to carry that much fuel and a heat shield to protect it during re-entry. At any rate, the U.S. experts said, Luna 15 was not a hazard for the approaching Apollo 11.

At precisely 10:33 a.m. EDT, Armstrong, Aldrin and Collins reached the midpoint of their trip to the moon, 120,003 miles equidistant from earth and moon. But their speed was down to 3,000 miles an hour, and the second 120,000 miles would take twice as long as the first. The astronauts gave their craft a three-second tweak of power from their spaceship engine to tighten their aim on the moon. So accurate was their launch the day before that this was the only correction in course necessary. But beyond that, it was comforting to know the big engine worked. It was the engine that would brake their speed to fall into lunar orbit, the engine that would blast them back toward earth again.

For all of the worrying about Luna 15, there were signs of friendship in the space race this day. From Poland, Soviet cosmonaut Valentina Tereshkova, the only woman to fly in space, wished the Apollo 11 astronauts well. In the same spirit, President Nixon announced from the White House that the Americans were carrying mementoes of the five men, Russian and American, who died in the space race. They would leave

Lunar Panorama—"A magnificent desolation," Aldrin called it. This view on the far side of the moon was seen as the astronauts returned to the command module.

Time Up—Told to get back aboard, Aldrin said reluctantly, "Roger, doctor. I understand," and he headed back to Eagle.

those mementoes on the moon. For the Americans, Gus Grissom, Ed White and Roger Chaffee, there was the shoulder patch of the Apollo 1 crew. For the Russians, Yuri A. Gagarin, the first man into space, killed in a plane crash in 1968, and Vladimir Komarov, the Americans carried medals given by their widows to Frank Borman during his Russian trip.

Said President Nixon: "The two men we hope will set foot on the moon represent all mankind. Their achievement will be the world's achievement. It is fitting, therefore, that the first lunar explorers carry with them some recognition of the sacrifice made by other space pioneers who helped to blaze their trail. There is no national boundary to courage."

Some 150,000 miles away from earth, the astronauts brought out the television cameras again. They started with a 21-minute view of earth. Collins narrated: "You're seeing the earth as we see it out our lefthand window. Just a little over half the earth... North America, Alaska, the United States and Canada, Mexico and Central America ... We can see the San Joaquin Valley, the Sierra mountain range, Southern California ... The greens do not show up too well."

Then he got playful. "Okay, world. Hang onto your hat. I'm going to turn you upside down." And he did. The shrouded blue planet did a lazy turn as he rotated the camera. "I'm making myself seasick," Collins said. "I'm going to put you right side up where you belong." They turned the camera on themselves, demonstrated push-ups from the floor and the ceiling in a world without gravity, showed off the loaded food locker, and

flipped a flashlight into the dark recesses of the spaceship. "Would you believe you're looking at chicken stew?" Collins asked holding up a plastic food bag. "All you have to do is add three ounces of hot water and blend for five or 10 minutes." "Sounds delicious," said earth, doubtfully.

The astronauts did some jogging in place, and demonstrated how much larger their world could be when ceiling and walls were floor as well. By now they had settled into routine. In suburban Houston where she watched the launch on television, Pat Collins had slept with the squawk box carrying the astronauts' voices near her head. But now she turned it off "to get some quiet for a little while." Janet Armstrong unpacked and cleaned her swimming pool. In Colorado Springs, the U.S. Aerospace Defense Command announced it had recorded Apollo 11 as the 4,039th manmade object in space, and one of 1,743 still in orbit. On the second day of flight, more than half of the states had followed President Nixon's proclamation of Monday, July 21, as a holiday.

Friday, Day Three of the mission, found Apollo 11 at the apex of that long gravitational hill between earth and the moon. At 1:12 p.m., EDT, the nose-to-nose spaceships passed the milestone where the moon's gravity becomes the more important influence. The astronauts were 214,000 miles from earth, only 38,000 miles from their rendezvous with the moon, leading their target like a hunter leads a duck. Their speed now was down to 2,000 miles an hour, but under the moon's gravitational influence, it began to build up again.

They were still flying in the so-called "barbecue mode" during rest periods and other inactive times, turning their spacecraft three revolutions an hour on its long axis, like a hot dog on a spit, keeping a new side constantly toward the flame of the sun. It was a cheap and effective way of maintaining a constant heat balance. Armstrong and Aldrin checked out the conditions of the Eagle, entering through the tunnel that connected the craft to the mother ship Columbia.

It was not only the taxi that would take them down to the moon's surface and bring them back again, it was also a prime reason the United States was winning the race to the moon. In the summer after President Kennedy had issued his moon challenge, the space experts had argued how to fulfill it. There were a number of ways, requiring varying degrees of booster strength—direct flight, launch from earth orbit, unmanned supply vehicles. Ultimately, the economics and the logic of flying into a lunar orbit, landing the lightest possible craft and saving the energy of the mother ship for the trip home, won out. The outcome was disposable, fragile Eagle.

The lunar lander, or Eagle, was the jurisdiction of Armstrong and Aldrin, who would fly it to the moon's surface. Columbia was Collin's responsibility. During another televised tour of the spaceship Friday, Armstrong shot a picture of Collins alone at Columbia's controls. "Hello earthlings," Collins said, smiling. "Is Collins going to go in the lunar module and look around?" asked Mission Control. "We'd like to let him," said Armstrong, "but he hasn't come up with the price of a ticket." The 96-minute telecast was so clear that earth viewers could see motes of debris floating in the weightless environment. The astronauts shot another picture of a miniscule earth appearing as large

Eagle Returns—Armstrong and Aldrin bore in on Columbia in a big step toward home. Earth is in the distance, 240,000 miles away.

as a golf ball fading into the dark beyond.

As Columbia and Eagle neared the moon, there was some renewed concern over Luna 15. Frank Borman called M. V. Keldysh, president of the Soviet Academy of Sciences, for details. Keldysh specified by return cable the details of Luna 15's orbit, and assured Borman it would not interfere with the orbit of Apollo 11.

Meanwhile, Armstrong, Aldrin and Collins coasted through the early phases of their flight plan, designed to conserve their energies for the minutes and hours ahead.

Those minutes and hours had been on the minds of the astronauts for some time. Buzz Aldrin, a Sunday school teacher, had even gone to his minister a few weeks before to talk over the meaning of the flight. And Aldrin's father had suggested that the astronaut read the Psalm 8 from the surface of the moon: "When we behold the heavens,

Strange Welcome—The first man to greet the astronauts was Navy Lt. Clancy Hatleberg, who scrubbed them and Columbia with disinfectant. All four men wear biological isolation garments.

the work of Your fingers, the moon and the stars which You set in place; what is man that You should be mindful of him, or the son of man that You should care for him?"

Day Four. Saturday, July 19. At 1:22 p.m., the astronauts fired their spacecraft rocket behind the moon, and fell into a lunar orbit. From that vantage point, they televised spectacular views of the moon to earth, pointing out such astronaut landmarks as Boot Hill, Diamond Back, Sidewinder, Apollo Ridge, and Mount Marilyn, informally dubbed for Jim Lovell's wife. They also reported some strange bright spots on the inner wall of a crater north of the spacecraft's orbit. "It seems to have a slight amount of fluorescence to it," Armstrong said. "The area in the crater is quite bright." But no one could tell at that distance whether what they were seeing was illusion, or evidence that the crater Aristarchus was hiding the signs of volcanic activity, signs that the moon, too, had a hot heart like earth's.

"The earthshine coming through the window is so bright you can read a book by it," observed Mike Collins. But Armstrong's eyes were taken with the moon. "The view of the moon is really spectacular," he said, ". . . well worth the price." The colors of the moon seemed dependent on the slant of the sun's rays. In twilight, the colors were gray or ashen. In full light, there were several shades of tan and brown. "We're getting our first view of the landing site approach," Armstrong said. "The pictures and snapshots brought back by Apollos 8 and 10 have given us a pretty good preview of what to look at here. It looks very much like the pictures, but it's the difference between watching a real football game and one on TV. There's no substitute for actually being there." Aldrin concerned himself with a final check of the systems in Eagle. "Everything is beautiful in here," he said. "Everybody is happy as a clam down here," said earth.

On the eve of history, perhaps men do not sleep well, or perhaps they are not meant

Ten Steps From Home—The Apollo 11 heroes walk 10 steps into isolation. A scientist followed and sprayed the pathway with germ-killer.

to. Before they slept Saturday night, their rest period was delayed an hour-and-a-half because of a pesky communications problem, finally tracked down. They were awakened at 7:02 a.m. Sunday, Armstrong with five-and-a-half hours sleep, Collins with six, Aldrin with five. It was the shortest rest period of the flight. They spent half an hour on breakfast. Mission Control beamed up the latest on their families, and the morning news. Aldrin was told his son had a visit to the space center with an uncle.

Then it was time to get down to business. Aldrin was the first into the Eagle at 9:20 a.m. Almost an hour later, Armstrong slipped through the tunnel to join him. From then on, they were Eagle. Collins was Columbia. At 12:32 p.m., they pushed a button that extended the landing legs of Eagle.

Thus did Columbia and Eagle, still linked together, arrive at this incredible time and place, out of sight and out of radio contact with earth on their 13th orbit of the moon. Some 100 hours had passed since they had left their home planet. Now they were 240,000 miles away from it, about to commit themselves to history. Behind the moon, Collins pressed a simple button. Latches clicked open. Springs gave Eagle a gentle shove. On earth they waited for word. Finally the radio signal came through. It was Armstrong's voice crackling with static. "The Eagle has wings," he said.

Now briefly they flew formation together, Collins looking over the weird little ship Columbia had borne this far. "Looks like you've got a mighty good looking flying machine there, Eagle," he said, "despite the fact you're upside down." "Somebody's upside down," replied Eagle. Less than half an hour later, Collins gave Columbia a spurt of rocket power and dashed some two miles ahead, allowing Eagle flying room. "See you later," he said. Eagle was on its own.

Again, they passed behind the moon, to that point in orbit where major changes are made, again out of sight of earth and out of radio contact. Armstrong and Aldrin tilted their little ship so that the rocket faced the direction of flight. When they emerged from behind the lunar shadow, the earth heard Armstrong say, "The burn was on time." Collins confirmed, "Listen babe, everything is going just swimmingly." The descent to the moon's surface had begun.

Eagle flew the long, looping arc, riding its tail of rocket fire like a brake, cutting into its 3,700 miles per hour speed.

"Current altitude about 46,000 feet," reported Mission Control. "Everything's looking good here."

Eagle: "Our position check downrange shows us to be a little off."

Mission Control: "You are to continue powered descent. It's looking good. Everything is looking good here."

There was total silence in Mission Control, except for the reassuring voice of the cap com, the business-like reports over the engineering and flight dynamics channels. "Two minutes 20 seconds, and everything looking good," reported Mission Control. "I'm getting a little fluctuation," said Eagle. "Looking good," said Mission Control. "Shows us to be a little long," persisted Eagle. "You are go to continue powered descent," insisted Mission Control. "You're looking good."

"Got the earth right out our front window," reported Eagle. The guidance computer on board was showing some variations. "You're looking great, Eagle, you're looking great," Mission control reassured. "You're go for landing."

"Roger, understand," said Eagle. "Go for landing, 3,000 feet . . . 2,000 feet . . . Okay, it looks like it's holding."

Armstrong's voice was clear, and as brisk as a stock market report. But his heart rate was running some 40 beats a minute higher than normal. Now something happened to send it to 156 beats a minute, but his voice never betrayed it. He saw the landing site below strewn with boulders. He overrode the automatic landing system, grasping the rocket controls in his right hand, skimming over the littered field, searching out a clear spot: "540 feet . . . 400 feet, coming down nicely . . . 200 feet . . . 100 feet . . . 75 feet, still looking good, drifting to the right a little. . . ."

At 40 feet billows of dust kicked up by the rocket rose around the craft. "Okay . . . engines stopped."

"Houston,''said Armstrong tentatively. A long pause. Then: "Tranquillity Base here. The Eagle has landed."

"Roger, Tranquillity," sighed Mission Control. "We copy you on the ground. You got a bunch of guys about to turn blue. We're breathing again."

The time was 4:18 p.m. Cape Kennedy time, Sunday, July 20, 1969. Man had landed on the moon.

In Mission Control, nearly 100 space agency experts jammed the viewing rooms, literally looking over the shoulders of the flight controllers sitting behind their consoles on the floor below. Among them were John Glenn, Tom Stafford and Gene Cernan from Apollo 10, Jim McDivitt and Walt Cunningham from Apollo 7. "It's probably a good thing Armstrong doesn't know what's going on here on earth," said Cunningham. "Neil's the calmest guy on the communications loop." It wasn't a time to be calm. All of the flights, all of the men had led to this moment. Flight director Eugene Kranz slapped his console in delight. Behind him everyone was cheering, applauding. Kranz suddenly realized that discipline had broken down. "All right everyone," he called out. "Get settled down." The day wasn't over yet. There were grander moments in store.

In the White House, President Nixon watched televised reports with Frank Borman. The last 22 seconds, he said, was more like half an hour. When he caught his breath, he sent the astronauts his congratulations. "It was," he said, "one of the greatest moments of our time."

In London's Trafalgar Square, crowds of men and women cheered and screamed with delight. In New York City's Yankee Stadium the scoreboard flashed, "They're On the Moon." The Yankee-Senators game stopped, the stadium filled with cheers, then there was a silent moment of prayer, and the 35,000 fans sang "America the Beautiful."

In Wapakoneta, Ohio, Neil Armstrong's mother stood outside her flag-draped colonial brick home and said, "I hope it will be for the good of all mankind."

The last minute difficulties were explained by Buzz Aldrin: "That may have seemed like a very long final phase. The auto targeting was taking us right into a football-field sized crater. There's a large number of big boulders and rocks for about one or two crater diameters around it. And it required us to...fly in manually over the rock field to find a reasonably good area."

Armstrong noted: "You might be interested to know that I don't think we noticed any difficulty at all in adapting to one-sixth gravity. It seems immediately natural to move in this environment."

Ahead, he said, was "a relatively level plain, cratered with a fairly large number of craters of the five-to-50-foot variety, and some ridges, small, 20-30 feet high. I would guess. And literally thousands of little one- and two-foot craters around the area. We see some angular rocks several hundred feet in front of us that are probably two feet in size and have angular edges. There is a hill in view just about on the ground track ahead of us. Difficult to estimate, but might be a half a mile or a mile."

"Be advised," said Mission Control, "there are lots of smiling faces here, and all around the world."

"There are two up here also," replied Armstrong.

"Don't forget the one up here," called down Collins on his lonely patrol. Then he added his compliments: "Tranquillity Base, you guys did a fantastic job."

"Just keep that orbiting base up there for us," Armstrong replied.

The first duties were to check out the spacecraft. That done, Armstrong and Aldrin concentrated on describing sights no one had ever seen before. "Out of the hatch," Aldrin said, "I'm looking at the earth, big and round and beautiful." The sun played games with the color of the lunar rocks around them. "Almost every variety of rock you could find," Aldrin said, looking out the window. "The color varies, depending on how you're looking at it. Doesn't appear to be much of a general color at all."

Eagle stood some four miles beyond its planned landing site. It was also on a slight tilt, but not enough to endanger takeoff. "The guys that said we wouldn't be able to tell precisely where we are are the winners today," Armstrong said. "We were a little busy worrying about program alarms and things like that in the part of the descent where we would normally be picking out our landing spot."

As the day progressed, the chores inside the spaceship took longer than expected. Armstrong first asked permission to set foot on the moon at 9 p.m., then 10, then 10:30. "We'll support you any time," Mission Control said. At 7:42, they began the arduous task of getting into the heavy-duty, double-visored space helmets, the backpack oxygen tanks, and the other protective items they would wear in a world so unlike their own.

Slowly, they bled the pressure from their spacecraft, letting oxygen out, vacuum in. At 10:40 p.m., Armstrong reported, "The hatch is coming open." Then, following Aldrin's instructions, he began to back out onto the porch of the spacecraft, taking care that his suit did not catch or snag in the narrow opening. It was slow going. His 185-pound suit, weighing only some 30 pounds in lunar gravity, was more a hindrance because of its bulk than its weight. Suddenly he was standing on the porch of Eagle, beginning the tentative steps down the nine rungs of the ladder. On the way he pulled a lanyard releasing an equipment shelf and a television camera. Now, on screens all over the earth, you could see the stark shadows, and there, swinging, searching, a boot,

HORNET + 3

Armstrong's boot. Bit by bit, the whole man appeared. Now, off the last rung, onto the saucer-like footpad. Then, cautiously again, unsure of what was below it, he stepped with his left foot, a size 9½ foot in a clumsy, awkward step. He pressed the lunar surface at 10:56 p.m. His first words were, "That's one small step for a man, one giant leap for mankind." For 20 minutes he walked alone on the alien soil of the moon before Buzz Aldrin followed the same backward route down the ladder to join him. Aldrin looked around and his first words were, "Beautiful, beautiful, beautiful. A magnificent desolation."

Armstrong walked cautiously at first, almost in a shuffle, then with growing confidence. He found the footpads of Eagle had pushed only an inch or two into the lunar soil after a four-foot drop. His own foot, he guessed, pressed in only a fraction of an inch. But he could see his footprints in the dusty surface.

At 11:42 p.m. Armstrong and Aldrin unfurled the Stars and Stripes and erected the rod that ran along the top to keep the flag taut in the airless, windless atmosphere of the moon. Aldrin stood back and saluted. Armstrong stood at attention. Only minutes before, the spacecraft commander from Ohio stood at the side of Eagle reading the plaque affixed there in a steady voice to a listening world. "Here man first set foot on the moon, July, 1969," Armstrong read. "We came in peace for all mankind."

His first duties were more plebian than that. He quickly found some bits and pieces of moon and stuck them in his pocket so that mankind would have something to show for the trip, even if it had to be ended in a hurry. He talked of the new soil: "The surface is fine and powdered, like powdered charcoal to the soles of my foot. I can see my footprints of my boot in the fine particles."

From the Oval Room at the White House came President Nixon's voice beamed by telephone and radio across 240,000 empty miles. "I just can't tell you how proud we all are of what you have done for every American," he said. "This has to be the proudest day of our lives. For people all over the world, I am sure that they too join with Americans in recognizing what an immense feat this is. Because of what you have done the heavens have become a part of man's world. As you talk to us from the Sea of Tranquillity it inspires us to redouble our efforts to bring peace and tranquility to earth. For one priceless moment in the whole history of man all of the people on this earth are truly one. One in their pride in what you have done, one in our prayers that you will return safely to earth."

Said Neil Armstrong, "It is a great honor and privilege for us to be here representing not only the United States but men of peaceable nations with an interest and a curiosity and a vision for the future."

In the daring minutes that followed, Aldrin loped across the lunar panorama before the eye of the television camera set up now to survey the Eagle and the men of the Eagle. Both men collected soil and rock samples, set up a metal foil shade to catch the subatomic particles blown through space by the sun's solar wind. They also set up a seismometer to measure tremors in the lunar crust, and a mirror-like device to reflect laser light back to earth and help measure the distance to the moon to an accuracy of six inches.

Even before they were done, scientists on earth were trying to study the moon with their new tools. The astronauts were learning about moving in lunar gravity. It was easier than in weightlessness. There was a tendency to lope and hop rather than walk, and they occasionally looked like phantom broken field runners moving in and out of sunlight and shadow, becoming almost phosphorescent in the brutal, blinding glare of the sun. "Isn't this fun?" Armstrong asked at one point. One thing you learn, they said, is to lean in the direction you want to go. Time was whistling by. The astronauts took photographs and movies, filmed the panorama of the moon and their own intrusive, bug-like images. Aldrin, trying to get core samples of the soil, had trouble hammering the tubes into the proper depth. "I hope you're watching how hard I had to hit this into the ground to the tune of five inches," he told Mission Control. "It almost looks wet."

The quality of the lunar dust was strange too. Aldrin noted its cohesiveness. "The color of my boot has completely disappeared into—I don't know how to describe it—a kind of cocoa has covered my boot," said Aldrin. Checking over Eagle, they noted there was no discernible crater below the ship, despite the dust stirred up by the rocket. They also noted that due to some sideways motion, two of the probes that sensed the surface were bent and one was broken. Otherwise Eagle was in good shape. The glare of the

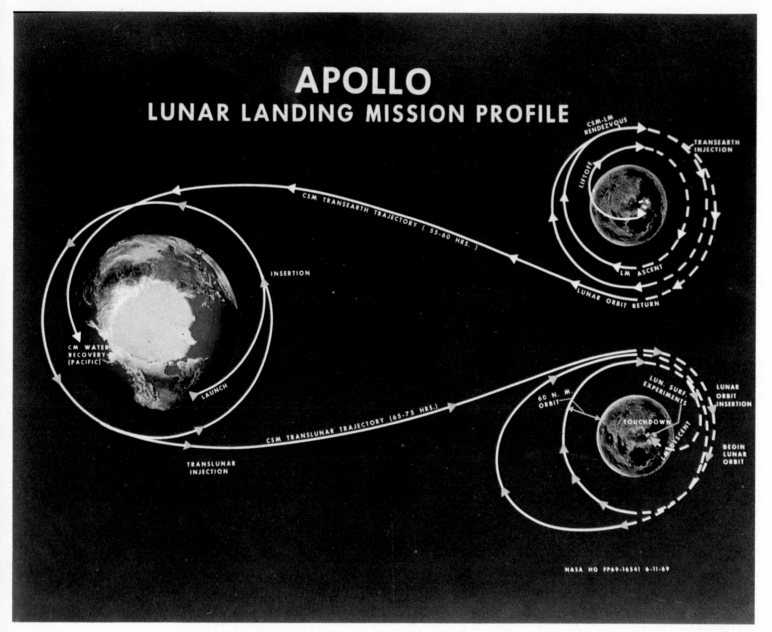

**Trip To The Moon—Flight path for Apollo 11.**

lunar sunrise caused both men some trouble seeing when they moved from light to shadow, even with the heavy filters of their visors. Suddenly the time was gone. Mission Control tried to hurry the astronauts packing up now to go home. They issued 10 minute warnings to each. "Roger, doctor," said Buzz Aldrin ruefully. "I understand."

They packed up everything that had to go in big white suitcase like boxes, the rock, the core samples, the bags of dirt, the foil that faced the solar wind. The seismometer, the mirror, the flag remained behind. At 1:11 a.m., Monday, July 21, 1969, they closed the hatch of Eagle behind them.

After some housekeeping chores, they tried to sleep in the seatless, uncomfortable cabin of Eagle. They didn't do well. There was perhaps an hour of rest through the night and that was fitful. At 1:54 p.m., Monday, they blasted off from the moon to catch up with their almost forgotten chauffeur, Mike Collins, riding Columbia in lunar orbit. As Eagle rose into the moon's sky, leaving the four-legged descent stage behind, Armstrong reported, "The Eagle is back in orbit, having left Tranquillity Base. They left a replica of their patch, an Eagle bearing an olive branch to the moon. Also behind they left the debris of the 21 hours and 36 minutes on the surface, the mementoes of the fallen fliers who paved their way, and the random footprints of men.

At just about that point in time, the Soviet moonship Luna 15, its mysterious job done, landed or crashed into the Sea of Crises, 500 miles away from the spot the Americans had walked.

Within six hours, Armstrong and Aldrin were sitting with Collins again in the relative comfort of Columbia. There had been a little trouble docking, but nothing serious. The astronauts actually made the transfer to the mother ship some two hours early. Eagle was cast away, to remain in space as long as its orbit of the moon would last. Eventually it too would crash to the lunar surface. Just 11 hours after they left the moon, they fired Columbia's engine for two-and-a-half minutes and drew a bead on the planet earth. Armstrong and Aldrin were tired, and Mission Control ordered up some sleep.

The trip back to earth was quiet and restful, if not quick. With hardly a problem, Columbia flashed through earth's sky and splashed down in warm Polynesian waters of the Pacific at 12:50 p.m. Thursday, July 24, eight days, three hours and 18 minutes after it took wing at Cape Kennedy, Fla. It landed just nine miles from the aircraft carrier *Hornet* and the eyes of President Nixon, on hand to greet the astronauts even if he could not shake their hands. They immediately went into the elaborate quarantine system in which they would remain until August 11, to protect the earth from any possible contamination from germs on the moon. The President faced the three men through a glass window in an isolation van, flanked by a Marine honor guard. All stood at attention as the Navy band struck up with "The Star Spangled Banner." The President then proclaimed, "This is the greatest week in the history of the world since the Creation."

"As a result of what you have done," he said, "the world has never been closer together." He invited them to a state dinner in Los Angeles on August 13. "Will you come?" he asked. "We'll do anything you say, Mr. President," Neil Armstrong answered. The three faces in the window were fresh and smiling broadly. Collins had grown a moustache on the flight. There was one moment of irony after the astronauts took their only open steps on the carrier, a 10-foot walk to the van from the helicopter that picked them up. Just after the door of the isolation van closed, a scientist in a short-sleeved yellow shirt quickly sprayed the pathway with disinfectant. It had to be the strangest hero's welcome ever.

Two separate freight planes carried the lunar samples back to the Manned Spacecraft Center in Houston. The astronauts didn't return until Sunday, via the *Hornet* to Honolulu and plane to Houston. The rocks and the lunar soil would remain a mystery for some time to come. They were covered with a black powdered material, which Aldrin said made them slippery. One rock at least was identified as a product of a molten process, but it didn't give away the secret to the origin of the moon. There would have to be more lunar landings, more samples from elsewhere on the moon

"One Small Step For A Man—
One giant step for mankind."

before science could draw any conclusions.

Three earthlings were put in isolation during those harried days following Apollo 11's return. First, a photographic technician touched a pack of moon film and got black moon dust on his hands. Then, two men working with the lunar rocks with their gloved hands inside a small vacuum chamber became contaminated when the gloves cracked open. The astronauts remained healthy, a trifle bored perhaps, but healthy in isolation.

The experiments they left behind and the rocks they brought with them were already beginning to speak of the moon's history. The seismometer recorded what was either an earthquake or the impact of a meteor somewhere on the moon. And a scientist said that the pieces of moon under study were "like an Aladdin's lamp. Rub them with the right instruments and they will tell you the secrets of the universe."

The adventure of space was also an Aladdin's lamp of sorts. It revealed once more that man's greatest deeds often arise from his strangest motives. A cold war between nations had given mankind a new planet to walk on.

# Beyond The Moon

Stretching endlessly beyond the moon is the ordered disorder of space. Nearest are the planets that keep earth company in shadowy orbits around the sun; and beyond them, the stars and the other solar systems of the Milky Way. And beyond, countless other galaxies yielding billions and billions of other suns. How far can man reach? How far does he dare dream?

For centuries, the moon was outside man's grasp. It dominated his night sky and his dark dreams. Now he stands on the moon, digs into its surface, its history and his own. Now he would prowl its highlands and valleys, climb its mountains, fly in space suits with backpack rockets over its surface. He would build on the moon, and establish a new platform for his curiosity.

Man is not smart enough to judge immediately what good it will be. But he has some glimmers of ideas.

He foresees orbiting stations around the earth, laboratories to make new materials in the gravity-free, perfect vacuum of space. He foresees observatories to search the sun, earth, moon, his own galaxy and galaxies beyond.

The earth. He would prospect his planet from space, use special cameras to search out secrets hidden below the earth's surface, discover what parts of earth best yield crops, then watch those crops for signs of disease and drouth. He would like to try to make optical glass without the stress of gravity, and he wonders what steel would be like forged in the vacuum of space. He thinks that observations from space might allow him accurate long range weather forecasts, and he grimly acknowledges that space may be what the military always seeks, the high ground. He knows he can map the earth better than it has ever been mapped before.

For instance, the U.S. Army Map Service has had a cooperative project with Peru for the last 25 years to map that rugged nation with aerial cameras. The laborious job is still going on. Yet, the Gemini 12 astronauts, orbiting the earth, showed that if they had carried the proper cameras they could have done it in just three minutes.

The sun. It has always dominated his life. Yet man knows little of the sun. He does know that if he would make the best use of his earth, he must first understand the star that holds it captive. With his new found ability to fly in space, he would send men into orbit with telescopes to watch the sun and probe its light for the answer to how the solar system began. And if he could measure the fluctuating power the sun beams to earth, he could predict well in advance his weather, the stability of his communications, the prospects for his crops. Is it too much to dream that he may one day set up power stations in orbit run by solar energy, beaming electricity to earth or moon?

The beginning will be a simple workshop, fashioned out of the hull of a dead rocket. Later he may assemble a 10-room house in orbit around the earth. Later still, who can guess?

The planets. Days after the Americans landed on the moon, Mariner space probes photographed the planet Mars to see what distance had denied the eyes of man.

Man's eyes, a creation of his life on earth, have a sensitivity only to visible light. But objects in the heavens emit all kinds of radiation, all kinds of light. Man has learned that what he cannot see often tells him more than what he can. The Mars probes viewed the red planet and inventoried its emissions of ultraviolet light. These emissions tell scientists what elements and what molecules exist. By knowing what kinds of chemicals exist on Mars they can better assess whether the planet began as earth did, whether life exists there, whether any life that does exist has the protection of an atmosphere, whether it is a suitable target for which to aim.

In the decades ahead man will reach beyond Mars and Venus. There are plans now to send unmanned satellites roaming through our solar system in the 1970s. The missions would take eight to 11 years, and the first Grand Tour, as it is called, would fly by Jupiter, Saturn and Pluto. The second would fly by Jupiter, Uranus and Neptune. Both would use the strong gravitational fields of the distant planets to bend and speed the Grand Tour satellites on their way like ricocheting billiard balls.

Like a subtle, persistent virus, man will spread through the solar system, and then beyond.

Just what part will America take in this invasion? Just how much are Americans willing to spend? Why should they do it at all? Why should any man?

As Armstrong and Aldrin landed on the moon, the space agency's budget had already been sliced well below the point that space planners said was the minimum for continuing programs. In his plea to Congress in 1969, space agency chief Dr. Thomas O. Paine warned, "At a time when the United States faces many problems in many fields, it is important that the national priority issues involved in moving ahead—and equally important, in failing to move ahead—be clearly understood. In my view, the Congress shares with the new administration a great responsibility for national leadership in aerospace at this time."

Whatever the United States would do in decades ahead, there was little question that man in some uniform, under some flag, would press ahead. The things that needed to be done would be done. The knowledge that beckoned would be followed. The earth would never be the same again, nor would man.

At the end of man's first decade in space, Prof. David P. Bloch of the University of Texas wondered whether the reach to the moon could ever be considered with earthly explorations, earthly adventures. It was far more, he said. If man was born of creatures which emerged from the ocean, now he was entering a new ocean, the ocean of space. Surely this too would reach into his very biology, his very mind, his conception of himself and the universe in which he lived.

". . . This may be an appropriate occasion," he wrote, "to take an Olympian view of ourselves. Life is one of the properties of matter. Its evolution has given rise to consciousness. Someone once said that man is the mind by which the universe contemplates itself. Now he is on the threshold of space. Some day it will matter little to what extent our individual or collective interests in space were motivated by curiosity, adventure . . . or what have you . . .

"I think that our reaching out into space is akin to our first clutch at a tool, or the poor fish's straining to be an amphibian, or to the development of the first nervous system. In its portent, it is of a different order of magnitude than Columbus' discovery. Except for some immediate practical considerations our reasons for reaching out are inconsequential."

A half century earlier, H. G. Wells wrote, "The past is but the beginning of the beginning, and all that is and has been is but the twilight of the dawn . . . A day will come when beings who are now latent in our thoughts and hidden in our loins shall stand upon this earth as one stands upon a footstool, and shall laugh and reach out their hands amid the stars."

That day has come.

# Index